THE BOOK
THE DIET
INDUSTRY
DOESN'T WANT
YOU TO READ

THE BOOK
THE DIET INDUSTRY
DOESN'T WANT YOU TO READ

JENNY MCDONALD

Heal your relationship with food
and most importantly yourself

First published in 2023 by Food Freedom Fairy Publications
Copyright © Jenny McDonald 2023

Jenny McDonald has asserted her right to be identified as the author of this
Work in accordance with the Copyright, Designs and Patents Act 1988.

ISBN: 978-1-3999-6764-8

Editing and design by Fuzzy Flamingo
www.fuzzyflamingo.co.uk

A catalogue for this book is available from the British Library.

I would like to dedicate this book to my daughter Nancy.
May she have a happy and healthy relationship with food.

This book is also dedicated to every woman who has ever struggled with their weight and their relationship with food. I genuinely hope that you find peace with food and with yourself.

Disclaimer

The information and material in this book are for informational purposes only. No material in this publication should be a substitute for medical advice, diagnosis or treatment. Always seek advice from a qualified healthcare professional regarding medical conditions and health concerns.

Contents

Introduction

'Lose a stone in a month! Three simple steps to shed pounds quickly! Drop a dress size in two weeks, the only diet for rapid weight loss.' These words used to excite me, and I would fantasise about the possibility of finally losing weight with speed and ease. If I could just stick to it for a few months, my life would be so different. I would be confident, I would like myself, respect myself. I could apply for a new job, find a loving partner, and, most importantly, food would no longer control me. Or so I thought.

Looking back, I never considered body acceptance and I certainly never thought about sustainable weight loss. As a yo-yo dieter, I would daydream about how quickly I could lose weight. Triggered by a special occasion, holiday or Christmas, I would think, *If I could be two or three sizes smaller by said event, I would feel so much better.* But that event came and went, and I was still a size twenty-four, struggling to find clothes to fit. I didn't think about the long-term goal of having a peaceful relationship with food. But you don't, do you? When you are suffering in a body you hate, all you want to do is take that pain away. And you will go to any lengths. From starving yourself, eating foods you hate, taking weight loss medications that leave you in embarrassing situations (if you know, you know), paying a fortune for fat-dissolving treatments, and even the last resort – surgical procedures.

The healthy eating message used to really annoy me. I would

roll my eyes at someone who told me to just eat healthy food! Yet now I understand the simplicity of nourishing your body. It took me a long time to get to this place, though. I had to work through a lot of other stuff. First, I had to accept that it was my responsibility and mine alone to get myself out of this situation. If there was going to be real change, it had to come from me. I had to find my inner strength to learn and develop my relationship with myself, as much as with food. I had to be brave enough to let go of unhelpful beliefs around food and be loving and compassionate towards myself as I evolved to where I am today. It has been messy; there have been tears, a lot of tears, and beautiful light-bulb moments that have opened up my world. It has been a learning process, and I will always be learning. I am definitely not perfect when it comes to food, but I don't want to be. What I want and what I finally have is to be able to eat absolutely anything without guilt. Be free to say, "No thank you," if I don't want something or I am simply not hungry. To be in tune with my body's needs. To have a dessert even if no one else is having one, to eat cake on a Monday without thinking I have ruined my week. To have complete 'Food Freedom'. And this is what I want for you: Food Freedom. And I am guessing, as you are reading this book, you want it too.

Before we dive in and I share my story, client stories and various tools and strategies to help you, I need to share a secret. I don't have all the answers, and I can't fix you. I once had a client that told her friends, "Jenny can fix me; she will reprogramme my brain!" Nope, I can't do that! BUT YOU CAN! It might not happen overnight, but with some small tweaks, you can feel completely different about yourself and food.

I started working on my relationship with food in 2004, and it is now 2023! However, many of my powerful learnings happened in the last four years, despite months of counselling and working within the weight loss industry since 2005. I now have a variety of tools I use myself and with my clients, and my aim is that you can use this book to get ahead a little quicker than I did! Having said that, there is also no rush. This is a process; think of it as learning a new skill. And of course, you will need to let go of some deep-rooted beliefs around food. Take your time, try not to focus on the end goal, just enjoy the journey.

I have written this book from my point of view, and I will share examples from women I have worked with. However, having also worked with over sixty men, I know many of their challenges with food are the same. However you identify, if you have a difficult relationship with food, I hope you will find this book helpful.

As for the title, yes, I chose it to catch your attention! I chose it in the hope that my readers would devour the contents of this book and never feel like they have to diet ever again. It is a long way off, but I would love 'dieting' to become a thing of the past so that future generations can live in harmony with their bodies and with food. This book encourages you to forget all of the dieting rules you have ever heard so that you can find your own path with food. Hence why the diet industry doesn't want you to read it! I can't claim to be 'anti-diet' because I originally had great success using diet products and selling them in a previous life. In fact, a meal replacement diet saved me from a spiral I had been stuck in for a long time. It allowed me the space I needed to step back from food. After my initial weight loss, I went on to work with meal replacement diets for many years. However, unless you are in the minority, embarking on any type of diet is pointless without some considerable mindset shifts and inner work. Unfortunately for some, dieting perpetuates disordered eating. I feel sad that I worked in this industry for so long before I recognised this. I can now see this was because I was still dieting myself – without realising it. Once my eyes were opened, I decided to close the doors on my thriving diet business and offer support through habit change coaching, deep mindset and energy alignment work. I recommend you read the book and thoroughly explore each activity before moving on to the next chapter. Like any self-help book or training, it works if you do the work. Reading this book will hopefully offer you a new perspective. However, implementing the processes I share will help you make long-term changes.

Whilst this book offers tools and guidance, it does not replace professional help. Our individual journeys with our relationship with food vary, and if you feel you would benefit from further support, I encourage you to reach out to an appropriate professional. In the back of the book, you will find lists of charities and organisations that provide advice and support.

CHAPTER 1

This Is Me

My Story

I sat on the bathroom floor sobbing. It was 7am. I pleaded with my mum, "Please don't make me go to school today." I felt hopeless; I was (and I hate the word) the 'fat' kid at school. That day I wasn't strong enough to face the torment. That day I couldn't face the comments such as, "Tree trunk legs!", "Fatty," or my unchosen nickname, "Big Mac." It was also swimming that day, which meant the whole class seeing me in my swimming costume and undressing with fifteen girls, all of whom seemed to be perfectly formed for their age. My clothes were homemade trousers because my legs refused to fit into 'normal' clothes. Occasionally I pushed myself, told myself I didn't care what others thought and wore a knee-length skirt. On those days, I usually ended up being late for school as I would get halfway and walk home to change. The brave juice would run out, and the thought of the torment and others staring at me got too much.

As my mum held me, she vowed (once again) to help me. She said we would work together and do whatever it took to 'get my weight down' to help me feel 'normal'. She would cook me different foods, make sure I had smaller portions, and we could exercise together to burn off calories. We signed up for a slimming club in a church hall. Looking back, I am sad and appalled that they accepted me as a member at such a young age.

Moments like this were just the beginning of my dieting journey. I was eleven or twelve.

Little did I know then that my tricky relationship with food would stay with me for life. Little did my mum know she and I were now fully signed up to the dieting culture, and we had joined my nan, a lifetime member. And for most, once you are in, you can't get out. It's like there is an unwritten pledge never to leave. I didn't know that the food restriction would trigger years of secret eating and a lifetime of questioning, counting, judging and worrying about everything that passed my lips.

Over the coming years, I occasionally found smaller versions of me, usually from strict rules around food and leaving the gym in a sweaty mess. But by the time I reached twenty-six, after fourteen years of dieting, I was a size twenty-four.

In November 2004, something changed; from somewhere, I found the strength to try again. I often say this strength came from being in a really low place. If I am honest, I was pretty miserable with my life. I had landed what I thought was my dream job in my local theatre. But my manager wasn't approachable, I didn't feel supported, only criticised. I would come home upset and desperate to leave; my confidence was at rock bottom, and my creativity disappeared. I hated who I had become with food, but it seemed to be the only thing that comforted me.

Fortunately, this time things were different because I had decided to work on my relationship with food whilst losing weight. I attended group cognitive behaviour therapy sessions to help me explore my eating. Alongside this, I followed a very low calorie meal replacement diet. I ate a combination of shakes and bars and drank water and black tea. Now, this type of diet is not for everyone, but for me, I needed and wanted a complete break from food. The weight came off quickly; it felt great to finally be 'in control' rather than food controlling me. For six months, I didn't eat conventional food. I lost six and a half stone and *thought* my problems were solved.

That was April 2005. And whilst my weight has stayed relatively stable over the years, I didn't realise until around fifteen years later that I still had what I would call a disordered relationship with food. The years of dieting had taken their toll, and the behaviour I developed around food was ingrained. To the outside world, I had cracked it, I was managing food, I was successful, but my new habits of under and overeating were taking their toll.

Lipoedema

I also didn't know I had a connective tissue disorder affecting my body. Despite the weight loss, my legs were still huge! I reached a UK size eight, yet my lower body was still a size fourteen–sixteen, and I could only wear wide-leg trousers.

My legs were, in my eyes, abnormal, ugly and unsightly. I never went swimming, even though this was the one thing I longed to do, and I had assumed I would feel able to do it once I lost the weight. The following year, in 2006, I was diagnosed with lipoedema – an abnormal collection of fat cells in one area or more of the body. Often characterised by larger legs and buttocks but, depending on the stage and type, it can also progress to other areas such as arms and stomach. Over the years, I have noticed this progression. Sadly, the condition is often misdiagnosed as obesity. Women worldwide are living with lipoedema and are entirely unaware they have it. Very few within the medical profession have experience or knowledge of the condition. Before my diagnosis, two plastic surgeons, whom I had approached for a thigh lift, had turned me away and told me I needed to lose more weight! I was fortunately diagnosed by the third surgeon I met. Until that moment, I assumed it was my fault, that if I hadn't got so big, I wouldn't have these awful legs. I thought if they removed the loose skin, my legs would at least look a little more 'normal'.

It is thought that it affects around 11% of women[1], but the lipoedema community believes it is much more! Below is a description of lipoedema taken from Talk Lipoedema's website:

"Lipoedema is a condition of the fat and connective tissue. It mainly affects women, and often starts to develop around late childhood, puberty or times of hormonal change. Most people first notice changes in the shape of their legs and ankles.
Some possible signs of lipoedema:

4

- *Fat tissue changes affecting the legs, buttocks, hips, tummy (abdomen) and/or upper arms.*
- *Fat 'bulges' developing around the knees or at the hips, for example.*
- *Changes are usually equal on both sides of the body.*
- *Body may look out of proportion; the upper body is smaller than the lower body.*
- *Waistline may be narrow in comparison to hips.*
- *Feet and hands may not be affected.*
- *The area may bruise easily, with broken blood vessels, and/or varicose veins."*[2]

If you feel you have lipoedema, there are support groups; some are listed in the back of this book. If you are fortunate enough that your GP is aware of the condition, then you are already ahead of most! There is literature available that you can take to your GP. If you are based in the UK, please contact Lipoedema UK and Talk Lipoedema. Other countries have their own charities and support networks, and the lipoedema global community is growing daily, particularly online. I have listed some online support groups at the back of this book.

Fortunately, over the past few years, there has been more research into treatment options. As lipoedema fat does not respond easily to conventional dieting and exercise, it was once thought the only option to remove the lipoedema fat was liposuction. However, there are women proving that dedicated self-care routines in the form of dry skin brushing (to aid the lymphatic system), massage and compression, alongside anti-inflammatory diets and specific exercise such as swimming, rebounding and strength training is a more conservative way to treat the condition.

So, did lipoedema drive my weight issues? Would I have managed my relationship with food differently if I had known I had the condition? I don't know, maybe, maybe not. I wonder if my condition would have been an excuse to stay stuck. Would I have thought, *I can't do anything about this*? Especially as lipoedema patients are often told they can't lose weight and their only option is surgery. If I had been told this, would I have even embarked on my weight loss journey or considered working on my relationship with food?

Becoming a Coach

I was overjoyed when I lost weight, and I wanted to help others to do the same. If I could conquer the one thing that had held me back for all these years, anyone could. I wanted to show other women the way out of the destructive cycle. To show them weight loss isn't about restricting food but about self-worth, self-love, changing beliefs, managing thoughts, emotions, and our relationship with ourselves, others and food. So, in 2005, I started work with a dieting company. I also trained as a weight loss coach, using CBT (cognitive behavioural therapy) and TA (transactional analysis) to help my clients explore their patterns around food and how they could make long-term changes. I spent ten years running small groups and supporting over a thousand ladies (and quite a few men) in changing their relationship with food. Within this setting, my clients could share their journey with others experiencing the same challenges. They were still dieting but diving far deeper into the root cause of their eating along the way.

Over the years, I noticed that those who attended meetings after they had lost the weight were far more successful. They continued to develop their new skills with their mind and food and kept their weight stable. Whilst we explored their relationship with food during the weight loss phase, when they reached their goal, their focus changed and the battle with food started again. Unfortunately, most of my clients didn't want to attend management meetings. They didn't value the meetings as much as they did in the weight loss phase, and I understood why. When we are in the 'this is amazing, I have finally lost weight' place, we don't necessarily want to focus on the details. We are just happy to be in a smaller body. Some ladies described it as finally being cured. They were grateful but didn't have time to continue to develop their relationship with food. They had holidays to take, shorts to wear and parties to attend. Plus, they didn't want to spend more money on themselves; they felt it was wasteful or unnecessary. They still had work to do on valuing themselves.

After ten years, in 2015, I closed my business and took a break from weight loss. I followed my other passions: theatre and teaching. I set up my own performing arts academy under a well-known brand. I loved my students; it was such a joy and an honour that parents trusted my team and me to teach their children. I thrived during productions and the buzz of live performances. But I missed helping women like me. I felt my purpose was to share my experience and knowledge in weight loss. I started to work for another diet company alongside my academy, and this was when I spotted the disconnect between diets and dieters. I couldn't believe I hadn't seen it before. How was it possible that so many women (like me) thought a diet was their only solution? And what's more that it was solely their fault when they didn't have the willpower to stick to it. I had to help these women see that it wasn't necessarily the answer and there was another way.

I began to make my way to where I am now, building my coaching business. I sold my academy and said goodbye to my 160 incredibly talented students. I decided to become a certified and accredited health and life coach. I am big on self-development, and I felt this would enhance my work and the skills I had to offer clients. Whilst completing this qualification, I had a revelation. Little old me, who thought she was doing well with food, was still stuck in the dieting cycle! I don't know how or why I had not seen this before, and I guess it developed over time, but I realised I was under-eating all week to save all my calories for the weekends. I can see how this started on a much smaller scale many years ago in a logical attempt to keep the weight off. Having a more indulgent night on Saturday when I was out with the girls was my thing, but this had now escalated to me standing in the kitchen at 9pm on a Sunday thinking, *What else can I eat? I have to be good tomorrow!* Thankfully, I explored this further, and I learnt that when I stopped restricting my food during the week, I was far less likely to want to overeat at the weekend because I didn't feel like I had deprived myself Monday to Friday. I am sure I learnt this many years ago, but like all things, it is simple and makes complete sense *when* you are ready to hear it. I also revisited my own nutrition or, as I like to call it, 'eating to nourish my body'. Again, I hadn't realised that my eating habits were pretty shocking, all developed in the desperate attempt to stay at my lower weight. I was helping my clients with this whilst doing the complete opposite myself! When I started eating properly, my mind was blown. I had been focusing so much on keeping the weight off that I hadn't paid attention to the patterns I had fallen into.

So, this is me, a forty-four-year-old woman who has just about broken free from dieting. And like every good fairy tale, there is a happy ending! The years of fighting with food and working in the dieting industry have made me who I am today. A coach who is passionate about helping others to break free from dieting and find peace with food.

What I have also realised is how broken the dieting industry is. A never-ending cycle we buy into in the hope it will solve our problems. Every January, there is a new quick-fix diet that promises to work. Even those diets that advertise healthy eating and creating a sustainable diet for life sell ready meals and processed food! Each class leader can be miles apart with their empathy, understanding, knowledge and skills. Even those at the top of their game are still managing a group of serial dieters who tell each other what they 'should' and 'shouldn't' eat and what delights they have 'got away' with eating and not gained weight. Some groups praise or even shame the dieters, depending on what the scales say. I know women who say they stick to their diet because they don't want to be humiliated when they weigh in. This makes me sad; it is no way for grown women to be living their lives.

Yet this is where we are and where many still believe they will find the answer.

In 2020, I launched the *Power Over Food Podcast*. I aimed to share my thoughts on shifting the needle within the dieting world. When I look back at the early episodes, I was still very much on a learning curve myself, but then we are always learning, aren't we? In 2021, I founded The Becoming You Academy®, a safe place for ladies to explore and develop who they are and their relationship to food. In the academy, the ladies work together in small groups; for many, this is more powerful than working alone. We find comfort in knowing we are not alone, and that others are experiencing the same challenges. The group allows women to share their thoughts and feelings without being judged. There is also great accountability; not only do the ladies want to succeed individually, but they also want each other to succeed. It is a pleasure and an honour to share my clients' journeys.

Why Write a Book?

I was inspired to write this book to reach more women who, just like me, have been on this treadmill for years. Battling food and weight is soul destroying, and I don't want anyone to stay in the cycle. I wouldn't wish this curse on my worst enemy, not even those school bullies. My aspiration for this book is to show an alternative method to tackling weight and food issues, hopefully far more rewarding, insightful and easier than dieting.

Anyone with a love-hate relationship with food will

understand the challenge is not the food. If you have scanned this book, you will see it has very little information about *what* to eat. Because the real challenge is *why* you eat. I have always said managing food is about how we manage life. When you have developed unhelpful habits around food, a diet will not fix it, whether food is a comfort when you are feeling upset, soothes you when you are angry, frustrated or lonely, or it is there to help you relax at the end of a long day, something to do when you are bored, or the food just tastes damn good! Aside from your feelings, you may have learnt that it is rude to refuse or leave food on your plate or that food is 'good' or 'bad', and you are 'good' or 'bad', depending on what you have eaten. And these are just a small sample of the thoughts, beliefs and emotions you are dealing with daily as you try to find the answer, to find the switch that will change things for you.

You dream of one day only eating when you are hungry and that food is always home-cooked, tasty, maybe even organic. You dream of sliding into that outfit hanging in your wardrobe for years, which is no longer in fashion, but you don't care because you know you will feel amazing in it! But with every failed attempt at dieting, you take a step further away from your dreams and hopes of cracking this food thing. You know there is a danger of never working things out. You may have even resigned yourself to always struggling with food. But you also know that if you never work this out, you have years ahead of you, always wondering if there is an answer. And if you don't solve this, you will have to accept that this is where you are staying, in a place where food will forever control your thoughts.

I certainly don't think we all need to be a specific size, weight or shape. As you will see, this book isn't about reaching your textbook weight. I also know that being smaller isn't always the answer we think it will be. This is about finding your happy place inside, finding peace within, accepting and loving who you are, whatever weight you are. The ultimate aim of this book is to promote self-love, a healthy mind and food freedom. I did question whether cutting all talk of weight loss from the book was a better way forward, but after countless polls with my followers and clients, I know that most want to lose weight *and* find food freedom. Note: when you develop a healthy relationship with yourself and food, your weight becomes less of a concern and you will naturally align to a place that is right for your body.

Whilst I will interchange between the phrases weight loss and having a peaceful relationship with food, please take what is relevant to you.

Aside from those who buy this book for their own journey, I also hope my book is read by partners out there who have a perfectly healthy relationship with food and can't quite understand their other halves' continuous battle. Maybe this book can help you with a new perspective on why it isn't as simple as just eating less. And for the awesome personal trainers who are passionate about helping their clients but just can't understand why they won't stick to their meal plan: maybe this book will offer a deeper insight into our battle.

You do not need to diet ever again. Just say that out loud, "I never have to diet again!"

A Life without Dieting

The best bit, there is a way out! You do not need to diet ever again. Just say that out loud, "I never have to diet again!" Can you feel a sense of relief saying that? Okay, I know it may be followed with, *But I want to lose weight, so surely I will still have to restrict my food*, thoughts. Nope! Not necessarily. Once you change your thoughts and feelings about food and about yourself, weight loss becomes much easier.

In this book, I will take you through the steps that I believe will help you rebuild your relationship with yourself and create a peaceful relationship with food. We start by looking at what it means to have a difficult relationship with food and why it is so damn hard to change it. It seems like we have pretty much everything stacked against us here! Then we will work on simply accepting where you are right now. This is huge. It is easy to come from a place of anger and frustration, but this will not serve you. Let's work from a place of compassion, letting go of judgement.

We will then look at building your awareness. Through doing this, you will get to know exactly where the cracks are and how to repair them. A crucial piece of the puzzle is getting to know the voice in your head. You will make friends with her – yep, no more fighting about what you should and shouldn't eat! Then you can start to work on valuing the amazing person you are and embracing self-love. You will discover your core beliefs, and look at your identity and how you see yourself in this world. I will also share a simple energy healing technique that you can use to release unhelpful beliefs. Before we touch upon the food, you will evaluate your relationships and lifestyle choices. As I said before, food is only a small part of the process. You already know what to eat, and believe it or not, your body knows what it needs. My guess is that you have stopped listening to it. Not intentionally – you just can't hear it with all the current diet noise!

When we look at food, you are simply going to play and experiment with your eating until you have everything you need to serve your body. There is no meal plan, only information and invitations to explore. You will not give up any food unless you choose to. I prefer to add in food rather than take it away! I will also touch on goal setting, values, willpower, motivation, stepping out of your comfort zone and the obstacles that get in your way. By the end of the book, you will have a toolkit that will help you not only with food but in all areas of your life.

So, are you ready to start your path to a healthy, happy, balanced life?

Yes?

Then let's do this!

CHAPTER 2

The Entangled World of Food and Weight

A Disordered Relationship with Food

Whilst there are a range of eating disorders recognised within the medical profession, many dieters may not meet the criteria for an official eating disorder. They would, however, display the same behaviours of being secretive around food, feeling shame and guilt after eating and suffering from low confidence and poor body image. For this reason, I would describe myself and the majority of my clients as having a disordered relationship with food. Over the following pages, I will share some of the behaviours of those caught in this cycle. The examples make up what is now commonly called 'diet culture'. First, let's acknowledge *why* there is an epidemic of disordered eating. There is no denying that the majority of men and women who struggle with food in the ways described in this book are closely linked to the desire to have a smaller body. From a young age, many of us have been conditioned that happiness, health and success come when you have a small, perfectly formed body. This message may have come from parents, family members, school friends, bullies, colleagues and the media. For years, the media have fat-shamed celebrities by highlighting their 'mum tum' or 'cellulite' on the front of magazines with headlines such as, "Linda has let herself go!" Whilst things are changing within this industry, we still have a long way to go to turn this around.

In addition, we have pressure from the medical community to fit within a specific parameter. Currently, the measure to determine whether we are under or overweight is the BMI (Body Mass Index) scale. According to government research, three-quarters of people aged 45-74 in England are overweight or obese.[3] However, the BMI chart is deemed by many as an outdated method of measuring. Studies suggest that the BMI measurement system is flawed[4] and that BMI cannot determine one's health condition. In other words, we can exist in a larger body and be perfectly healthy.

I genuinely believe that if we did not strive to fit into the perfect mould, whether that is a healthy BMI or, in the words of The Beautiful South, 'a perfect ten', we would never have started on the journey of calorie restriction. If society were accepting of different body shapes, if we had never become body conscious in our younger years, dieting would cease to exist. And if dieting didn't exist, then would the following examples be alien to us?

Yo-Yo Dieting

Once you become stuck in the dieting cycle, it seems hard to break free. Many of my clients have said, "I can't remember a

I genuinely believe that if we did not strive to fit into the perfect mould, whether that is a healthy BMI or, in the words of The Beautiful South, 'a perfect ten', we would never have started on the journey of calorie restriction.

time when I wasn't either on a diet or thinking about starting a diet." We spend weeks if not months restricting food to lose weight for holidays, weddings and other social events, then once the occasion has passed, we ease off and reward ourselves with the food we have missed. When you think about it this way, it is quite crooked, isn't it? Eventually, we slip back into our old ways of eating, and gradually the weight comes back on.

Interestingly, the statistics show that 80% of people who intentionally lose weight regain it within five years.[5] Yet most still see dieting as the answer. There are many factors that cause weight gain, which I will come to in the next section of this book. One of the biggest reasons I believe we regain weight is because we approach diets as something we hop on and off. We return to our old eating patterns when we stop dieting, whether because we have reached a smaller size or because we just can't face another day starving ourselves. Most of us will have spent years eating for reasons other than physical hunger. Going on a diet for most is pretty pointless. We need to work on our mindset.

The Constant Pressure

When trying to stick to a diet, be it counting calories, no sugar, low-carb or other methods, it can create an obsession with food, the worry about overeating and exceeding daily allowances. You substitute favourite foods for a 'diet' version that is less satisfying and often disappointing. You eat what you are 'allowed' to eat and therefore lose touch with your body's real cues. Even when you feel hungry, you work hard to ignore the pangs. The constant pressure to stick to the diet and not waver leaves you digging deep for the magic willpower to hang in there.

Good or Bad

When talking with friends, you find yourself saying, "I have been perfect this week," if you have stuck to your diet or, "I have been awful this week," if you have eaten off plan. Another common phrase is, "I've been naughty." Again, this type of self-talk comes from years of dieting. We have learnt that if we do as we have been told, we are good, and if we break the rules, we are bad. However, it is not as simple as sticking to the diet. Not only are we fighting against our body's natural need for food, but we also have the added pressure of our emotional hunger. Maybe you fancy some chocolate or a glass of wine, but you know that would take you over your allowance. So, you decide to skip a meal to stay within your calories. But the chocolate or wine doesn't fill you up; therefore, you are still physically hungry. You tell yourself you can't have anything else because you have been 'bad' by eating the chocolate. The chocolate you have eaten is unlikely to have a balance of nutrients that will satisfy you, but you go to bed early in an attempt to distract yourself.

This type of good/bad thinking perpetuates through the day and the weeks that you are restricting food until you finally give in and accept you are always going to be a foodie, and you will have to learn to like yourself as you are. (At least until the next time you feel the urge to lose weight!)

Justifying What You Have Eaten to Others

Ever heard yourself say, "I only had a sliver of cake," as you hold your fingers together to the point that no cake could even fit between them? I used to do this all the time! Worried that others would judge me for eating cake, I would ensure they knew it was only a small slice. I was also justifying what I had eaten to myself to ease the guilt I was feeling. The same would happen when standing in front of my slimming club leader. Knowing I may be criticised, I would lie about what I had eaten.

Whilst we attend clubs to be held accountable for what we have eaten, having a critical or judgemental leader will not help you long term. I have lost count of how many clients have said, "I need you to tell me off," or, "I need you to be strict." Whilst this may work on a short-term basis, what happens when you become tired of pleasing, of being the good girl? Or what happens when the 'teacher' is on holiday, and you decide there is no one to tell you off? Do you rebel? For the coachee, a relationship with a coach may feel like that of a child and teacher. They look to them for boundaries and rules. They like to please them and don't want to disappoint. Yet a well-trained coach will understand their role is not to judge or scold, it is to nurture and teach compassion for oneself. To encourage curiosity and learning, to gently challenge and hold the space.

The Eat-Starve Cycle

Maybe you starve yourself in the quest for weight loss, only to overeat when your body and mind can no longer endure the strict regime you have forced upon it. You feel an uncontrollable urge to eat and eat large quantities of food; after you have eaten, you feel shame and disappointment. You flip between all or nothing. For example, "I am totally in control; I will not eat anything other than fruit today," to, "I can't control myself. I am going to eat everything today and start again tomorrow."

Secret Eating

You may eat in secret because you feel shame or guilt about the quantity or types of food you are consuming. Restricting food makes you want it, but you feel like you shouldn't. In these moments, our inner self works out a plan: "If I eat it in secret, no one will know!" For years, I lied about what I had eaten. I also developed a fear of being hungry. If I was going for dinner with a friend, who, in my opinion, didn't eat a lot, I would eat toast or crumpets before I left the house. This made me feel calmer as I knew I wouldn't be hungry and could also choose a smaller or healthier option in front of them. I thought I could fool them into thinking I had a perfect diet.

Emotional Eating

You may use food to regulate your emotions. To soothe uncomfortable feelings such as loneliness, anxiety, stress, boredom and frustration. The comfort found in the eating process is often short lived but it provides a distraction and sensation that at the time hits the spot. The emotions are not always negative and I certainly find myself overindulging on happy occasions too. When food is used occasionally in this way, it is not an issue and doesn't have a negative impact on one's life. But when it becomes the substance you rely on to get through the day, it soon takes over your world.

The Obsessive Counting

Counting steps, calories in, calories burnt, carbohydrates eaten, the list is endless. Maybe you use exercise to balance what you have eaten. Perhaps you are meticulous when weighing your food and track every mouthful on your app. You may even do this with pride; you are the queen among your fellow dieting friends because you know all calories, from what is in an apple to a wholemeal wrap. Yet you still can't seem to make it work for you.

You may think *I need to measure what I am consuming to eat less, to be in control*, but if you have been counting for years and still find yourself reading this book, I think it is safe to say counting isn't working for you. Or at least it isn't working for you as you had hoped. But don't despair because you are about to find strategies that do work.

If you can relate to one or more of the dieting behaviours I have shared, you are certainly not alone and, as I will explain in the next chapter, this is definitely not your fault. However, you are the only person who can change your future relationship with food. But with the right tools and a huge serving of self-compassion, you can do this.

With the right tools
and a huge serving
of self-compassion,
you can do this.

CHAPTER 3

It Is Not Your Fault

I want you to know that this is not your fault. I want you to know that *I know* you couldn't have tried any harder than you already have. I know you have studied the plans you have followed, asked questions, and been really keen to make it work. I know it has been an emotional roller coaster, from anger and frustration to sadness. I know most of you have cried more than once over your weight, not just cried but sobbed. And if you are still blaming yourself, I hope this next chapter will help you to have compassion for yourself, allow you to calm your inner child, and help you and her acknowledge the challenges we face when it comes to releasing weight. I hope it will also help you understand why weight loss is so damn hard, especially when the solutions we are offered don't work!

We Are Programmed to Eat

The first thing I would like you to consider is that humans are programmed to eat. And the desire to eat is vital for our survival!

I want you to know that this is not your fault. I want you to know that I *know* you couldn't have tried any harder than you already have.

As Dr Andrew Jenkins describes in his book, *Why We Eat (Too Much)*[6], we need a source of energy, to survive, to breathe, think and move. Just like a vehicle needs fuel, and your computer needs electricity, we need food, water and sunlight. Your body is the most intelligent and complex computer you will ever own. It has automated systems to keep you alive, including finding pleasure in food so that you eat it and stay alive.

When our body needs fuel, it lets us know by releasing the ghrelin hormone. Cue hunger pangs! So, in most circumstances, we then eat to satisfy our hunger. Our brain knows that we are filling up with fuel and this is good for survival; therefore, it releases the feel-good chemical dopamine. Now, if you have eaten some fruit or some chicken, your brain will release a small amount of dopamine, but if you eat, let's say, chocolate, high-sugar foods or highly processed foods (that are obviously designed to taste way better than chicken), your brain is likely to release more dopamine. So, in simple terms, you may experience more pleasure when you eat high-sugar foods, which means you are more likely to want them again and again. If something makes you feel good, you want to do it again. How often have you had an enjoyable evening with friends or a wonderful holiday, and you plan to recreate the experience because it felt so good? The same happens with food!

Hundreds of years ago, our survival relied on hunting for food. Nowadays, not only are we less active, but thanks to the food industry, we have instant access to high calories.

Genetics and Hormones

Hormones have a significant impact on our appetite. If the cortisol level in your body is high because you are suffering from chronic stress or lack of sleep, you are likely to feel hungrier. The same happens if you produce excess insulin (linked to being overweight and having a diet high in processed foods). Then we have leptin, which is responsible for appetite, metabolic regulation and energy expenditure. Again, if leptin resistant, our hunger can become dysregulated.

Hormone imbalances have an impact on not only our appetite but also our metabolism and how our body stores fat. When there is an imbalance of hormones, our body's functions can be disrupted, which can lead to weight gain or difficulty losing weight.

There is also evidence that genetics affects our body shape and size. Our ancestors' lifestyles and diets may have an impact on whether we are predisposed to storing fat.

Whilst the food we consume will always be fundamental, these are additional considerations that affect our overall eating patterns and fat stores.

Our Connection to Food

Our first experiences of the world are to be held and fed. As babies, we express the feeling of hunger by crying. Once we let our parents or caregivers know we need food, the need is usually met, and whilst eating, we are cradled and loved. Whilst we cannot remember these moments, the sensation of eating food and feeling secure and happy is likely to be stored in our system.

The feeding experience may not have been the same for every newborn, as Julia Buckroyd explains in her book, *Understanding Your Eating*[7]. If food and love were scarce in the early years, it is possible that, as adults, we may eat to fill our needs once the food is readily available. This link continues in our early years. As tiny humans, we learn to make sense of the world. Each day we receive new information from our parents, teachers, grandparents and caregivers that shapes our behaviour and how we live our life. Psychiatrist and psychologist Eric Berne, the founder of Transactional Analysis[8], calls the information we are given our 'parent messages'.

I wonder what messages you received about food. Was food used as a reward? If you did well at school, were you treated to sweets on the way home? Were you told not to leave the table until you finished your dinner? Or were you often praised for clearing your plate? I also wonder how many of those messages you still listen to today. Do you 'treat yourself' with food after a long day at work? Do you always clear your plate, even when you are stuffed? How often have you heard yourself say, "I have been good today"? Or "I deserve it"?

Do you recall food being offered as a comforter? If you were hurt or upset, did a piece of cake make it all better? Let's imagine a three-year-old child running in the garden. She trips and grazes her knee. Her mother scoops her up, cuddles her and says, "Would you like an ice cream? Would that make you feel better?" The little girl nods and dries her tears. And potentially forms the learnt belief that food (often high-sugar food) helps you to deal with pain and trauma.

Suppose the little girl continues to self-soothe as an adult when she experiences pain and upset such as relationship breakdowns, difficulties at work, money worries, illnesses, trauma and loss of loved ones. In that case, food becomes the go-to solution.

As an aside, I think many of my readers will agree that food doesn't solve the problem; in fact, it often perpetuates it. We start with the issue of, let's say, an argument with our partner. We eat to feel better, but we still have the same uncomfortable feelings, plus the added frustration and guilt from eating a whole day's worth of food in one evening.

I am not saying our parents are to blame; we must remember that they, too, have learnt behaviour. The love and care they have given has likely been passed on from their caregivers. Messages are often passed down from generation to generation until someone breaks the chain. And, for our parents or indeed for their parents and their grandparents, food may have been scarce, food may not have been so readily available, they may have lived through a time of rations or a time when money was tight, and it was a daily challenge to make the food stretch around the family.

They may, like my family and many families, have learnt the message that food = love, and if I provide you with food, I am caring for you. I am showing you love. We all know someone who won't let you visit without giving you a biscuit or piece of cake with your cup of tea!

A World of Instant Gratification

We are now living in a world of instant gratification. If we want something, we can have it. If you want to buy a new car, you can go out and get one; you don't have to save, you can purchase on finance and drive it away within twenty-four hours. Or at least you could until the recent shortage of new cars! If you need something from an online store, such as new clothes for a night out, it can be delivered the next day. We no longer wait until Christmas for new boots and a winter coat. We often go out and buy what we need as we need it, or, should I say, *want* it. With food, it is no different; if you want a takeaway, you can often have it delivered to your door within thirty minutes. Whilst this is an exciting time to be alive, stuff and food have become our fix.

Aside from the instant fix, isn't food just everywhere? Whether attending a work meeting, catching up with family, or celebrating a milestone birthday, anniversary, wedding or funeral. From the friend with coffee and cake to biscuits in meetings, the pub meals to the birthday buffet. What's more, the food is indulgent and not necessarily food to be eaten daily. Years ago, we would not have overindulged so often, but nowadays it is easy to attend several occasions in one week which involve heavy meals, cakes or pastries. And, if you have a problematic relationship with food, these events often become more about the food than the occasion.

Sometimes I will ask my clients what they look forward to apart from the food. I ask, "Would you enjoy your night out if you were only going to meet for drinks?" Sometimes we need to step back and consider why we are meeting friends. Is it just to eat? Or is it to catch up because you haven't seen them in months? Whilst food can still be part of the meeting, it is helpful to take the view that food is less significant, and the real excitement comes with meeting the new baby or celebrating the engagement. Changing our perspective allows us to reassess the importance of food.

You may be frustrated or anxious because these occasions throw you off plan. You may even approach the situation promising yourself that you will choose something healthy and within your allowance. But then your internal voice and the external pressures to partake become too much. You give in, promising yourself you will make up for it the day after, but then the internal chatter starts. "Why did you eat the chips?", "You said you were going to stick to your plan", "You are never going to lose weight if you carry on like this!"

The Pressure to Eat

"Go on, one won't hurt."
"You are not dieting again, are you?"
"It won't be the same if you don't have a drink."

We can often feel pushed into eating and drinking. For various reasons, other people love to have their say on what you do with food. This pressure sometimes comes from a place of love; maybe others notice that dieting makes you miserable. They just want you to be happy. In their eyes, you are not yourself when restricting food, you are at ease when eating freely. (Or so it looks to the untrained eye!) To some extent, they are correct – if you were eating food from a

Changing our perspective allows us to reassess the importance of food.

place of freedom and true enjoyment, you would be at your happiest, right?

Others may want you to stay stuck. Often this comes from a place of fear. They are concerned that you becoming a smaller person will shift the balance in your relationship. Whether it is a friend, colleague, parent or partner who would prefer you to stay where you are, notice it does not always come from a conscious place. Sometimes the other person is unaware of their sabotaging behaviour. Maybe they think they are helping you by encouraging you to eat freely. We will explore relationships in chapter eleven.

Dieting Confusion and the Food Industry

Like my clients, you may feel confused and overwhelmed with all the information you have received about what to eat! You have been bombarded with 'the best', 'the quickest' and 'the most sustainable' way to lose weight. From keto to meal replacements, low-carb to vegan, calorie counting to fasting, I am sure you have dabbled in most, if not all. I even tried food intolerance testing thinking it would give me the magic answer. I gave up dairy for a week, gained 5lbs and then went back to eating dairy! (Insert facepalm emoji!) This was because I stopped eating dairy and ate extra food to compensate for the restriction! Now, this is not to say I am not intolerant to dairy. I limit dairy these days as it can cause inflammation in lipoedema patients. However, I was in a desperate place at that time, searching for the answer. It wasn't until years later that I realised the answer was within me.

We are also up against the food giants and their deep pockets. Their job is to make food taste delicious and leave us wanting more. They spend thousands testing and tasting to create an array of processed goodies, packaged up in bright colours, that we just can't resist. Jump back in time to sixty years ago, there were very few supermarkets, let alone the abundance of choice within them. Today we are faced with aisles of processed junk! In reality, everything you need to nourish your body is in the supermarket's first two to three aisles.

I hope that reading the above reminds you that there is a considerable amount stacked against anyone trying to lose weight, and if you have got as far as reading this book, a book that isn't a diet plan, you are ahead of many! Once you start to unravel your behaviour around food, you will be able to build trust and an appreciation of yourself that will be stronger than ever.

You are about to, as they say, "Change the habits of a lifetime." And yes, it can be done! What's more, it is far easier than spending the rest of your life torturing yourself with restriction and self-loathing. I am not saying it will always be easy – there may be tears – but I promise you, if you hang in there, it will be worth it. You may wish to buy yourself a notebook for the ride, as there will be many opportunities to make notes and reflect.

So, are you with me? Are you ready? Then let's do this!

CHAPTER 4

Making Friends with You

Over the following chapters, you will work on getting to know yourself on a deeper level. This will be fundamental to creating a relationship with food and yourself that you love. I will guide you through simple activities which allow you to reflect and connect with your true self. We will start with making friends with your inner voice, which many of us battle with when it comes to food. If self-development is a new experience, I invite you to lean in and commit to enjoying the process. I recommend gifting yourself some regular time where you can focus on you, when there are no distractions. When transforming your relationship with food, you are learning a new skill; it takes time, practice, knowledge and, most of all, patience! The same as learning to play an instrument. Think about the steps to becoming a proficient piano player. Think of the number of bum notes you would play! How long would it take to read the music or play competently with both hands? I invite you to view developing your relationship with food and yourself in the same way. Be patient, allow time for mistakes, and don't worry if you play off-key! If you don't throw the towel in, your goal will always remain, so each time you feel you have overindulged or hit that dud note, take time to reflect and learn. Over time, you will soon fine-tune your eating.

When I talk about your inner voice or inner self, I am referring to the voice that tells you that you will never lose weight, always struggle with food, are not good enough and that you are destined to have this battle. The voice that encourages you to eat and then tells you that you are stupid and have no willpower. Some call it the monkey mind or chimp; others liken it to having a devil on their shoulder. Whatever you have called it in the past, I think we can agree that your inner voice plays a huge part in what you eat. I bet you have had plenty of arguments with her about what you should and shouldn't eat. I wonder how many of these arguments you have won.

Inner Voice: "Go on, just eat it; you know you want to."
You: "No, I am fine. I don't even want it."
Inner Voice: "Of course you want it. It's your favourite!"
You: "No, I am sticking to my diet."
Inner Voice: "You can start again tomorrow."
You: "But we both know that won't happen, and I won't start again until Monday."
Inner Voice: "Okay, start on Monday."
You: "But then another week has passed!"
Inner Voice: "Yes, but then you could enjoy the weekend knowing you will be really good next week."
You: "Oh, I always do this. I don't want to start Monday! I just want to lose weight and eat normally."
Inner Voice: "Well, maybe you will feel more motivated on

Some call it the monkey mind or chimp; others liken it to having a devil on their shoulder. Whatever you have called it in the past, I think we can agree that your inner voice plays a huge part in what you eat.

Monday. I don't think today is a good day to be focusing on your food choices."

Do you recognise this conversation? Whatever the outcome, it's damn exhausting battling with her, and it will never help you achieve what you are aiming for.

So, how about you become her best friend?

"What?!" I hear you say! Okay, hear me out. Let me offer a different perspective, a new way of hearing your inner voice. I want you to think of this voice as another part of you, a part of you that is desperate just to feel safe and loved. A part of you that is working hard to keep you safe from feeling pain or discomfort. A part of you that has learnt food makes you feel better. And a part of you that feels safe in this place, despite being uncomfortable. Why? Because it is familiar, it is what she knows. It is how her life is and has been for some time. She doesn't know if you can find peace with food. She has watched you try and fail so many times, which means this whole process is scary. If she feels that your actions may cause you any kind of suffering, she will do her best to stop this from happening. And unfortunately, that includes telling you that you can't do it, that it won't work, and sabotaging you any way she can!

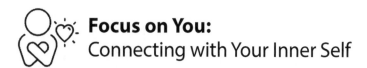

Focus on You:
Connecting with Your Inner Self

In a moment, I would like you to close your eyes, take a few deep breaths, allow yourself to settle, go within and connect with your inner self.

Step 1: Finding Your Inner Self

As you sit quietly I invite you to find the part of you that struggles with food. The part of you that you argue with on a daily basis. Now I want you to understand what part of you she is. Is she your younger self, twenty-five years old and getting ready for a Christmas party but feeling frumpy in her sequin jumper? Or is she of school age, comparing herself to her peers and wishing her body was smaller? Or maybe she is an up-to-date version of you? Once you have made that connection, take a moment to make the image of her crystal clear. What is she wearing? Where is she? Who is she with, or is she alone? Notice how she feels about herself. What makes her smile? What makes her sad? What are her worries and fears?

Step 2: Reconnecting with Your Inner Self

Now imagine sitting down next to her; ask if you could have a moment of her time.

Once you are both settled together, I would like you to thank her for the support she has given you over the years, tell her how grateful you are that she is with you. Tell her that you understand that everything she has ever done for you was to keep you safe. Thank her for doing her best with the knowledge and information she had.

Remember, if she learnt that sweet food brought you comfort or that bread filled an emptiness, then it

41

is no surprise that she has automatically offered this as a solution whenever you have felt discomfort or pain.

Step 3: Negotiate with Your Inner Self

Gently explain how this way of eating is causing you to feel and how you would like to make some changes. Ask her if she is willing to work with you.

She may say no or not answer. If this is the case, ask her what she is scared of. What worries her about making changes around food?

Is the concern that you are going to restrict food again?

If this is the case, you can reassure her there is no restriction here – certainly not in this book!

Perhaps she thinks you will take away the pleasure of eating or, even worse, take away your coping mechanism.

Again, we are not planning to take away any food, and you will learn other strategies to help you move forward. That's not to say you will never again turn to food, and if you do, it is entirely okay.

Perhaps she feels the pain when you lose weight and then regain it?

Tell her you understand, and you feel it too.

Maybe she doesn't want you to go through that all over again; she doesn't want to feel that shame of failing.

Tell her you are with her, you know that feeling too well, and you promise her there is no more shaming or failing here. There is nothing to fail at. All you are asking her to do is to work on having a better relationship with food.

Maybe she doesn't know how the world looks as a smaller person.

Or doesn't want the attention or pressures she thinks will come with a smaller body.

Sometimes we promise to do things once we are smaller; apply for a new job, start dating, get married, or leave the toxic relationship. You can see why it may be easier for her to say no, this is too scary. Sometimes we stay in a body we are not happy with as it keeps us safe.

If this relates to your inner self, reassure her that you will take this one step at a time. There is no pressure to make any big changes. All you want to do is take small steps.

Whatever her concerns, do your best to understand, explore and reassure.

When you feel ready, thank your inner self. Tell her you are always here, will continue to check in with her and invite her to reach out whenever she needs to.

Step 4: Communicate Regularly

Keep the lines of communication open.

Schedule a set day when you can check in with your inner self.

If you notice her trying to sabotage your efforts, ask her why. What is going on for her today?

Reminder! This is not about never eating something you once deemed 'unhealthy' or 'bad food'. This is about making choices each day that serve you. Sometimes, that may be eating the ice cream, which is okay.

Christine's Story

Christine was a single forty-eight-year-old mother of two grown-up sons. She worked in the corporate world and was one of few women in a very male-dominated environment. When we met via video chat, Christine's exact words to me were, "Jenny, I am so successful, but I feel that the men in the workplace judge me because of my size. I have this cloud hanging over me, and that cloud is food. It teases me. It haunts me, and I just wish I could never eat again. I think I would be okay if I didn't eat."

I understood and empathised with Christine's words. I remember saying many times, "I would be okay if I didn't have to eat." I feel sad that so many of us get to a stage where we hate food so much that we don't want to eat or can't enjoy the pleasure of eating because of the battle in our minds.

When Christine connected with her inner self, she found her fourteen-year-old self was very fearful. Christine promised her that it was safe to talk. As I guided her through some questions, she shared her concerns about giving up all the foods she loved and never eating them again. What would there be to enjoy after a long day at work? Would she still be able to have a glass of wine? Her inner self also didn't know what it was like to be smaller. What if people treated her differently? What if it changed her friendships or her relationship,

Reminder!
This is not about never eating
something you once deemed
'unhealthy' or 'bad food'. This is
about making choices each day
that serve you. Sometimes, that
may be eating the ice cream,
which is okay.

particularly with her sister? Helen, her sister, also struggled with food and didn't like Christine losing weight. They once had a big argument over Christine's weight loss method after she followed a meal replacement diet and lost seven stone. Her sister told her she looked ill and should stop immediately. They had a huge row and didn't speak for almost a year, in which time Christine had regained most of her weight. Her internal programming confirmed her bigger body was safer.

Other reasons emerged as we continued to work with Christine's inner self. She was scared of losing weight and never finding a new partner. She said she could cope with being unlovable at this weight, but what if she lost weight and still didn't find a partner? Christine's self-worth was very low, so we started working on this immediately. You will find exercises in the next chapter to help you increase your self-worth. As Christine started to value herself, she began to recognise that her weight did not define who she was. As she developed a love and appreciation for herself, her world changed. She relied less on food, her weight decreased. She managed her relationship with her sister and even taught her some of the tools she had learnt. Christine is now dating and says she feels more confident than ever because she finally knows her worth.

CHAPTER 5

Loving You

The term 'self-love' is everywhere nowadays. We are now encouraged to love ourselves, whatever our size, and I totally agree! If you use social media, you will know there are ladies of all shapes and sizes with beautiful stretch marks and wobbly bits embracing their curves and promoting self-love. However, if you have spent years loathing your reflection, it doesn't matter how many self-love gurus you follow, self-love can be challenging. In this chapter, we will start work on raising your self-worth and self-esteem. Let's get you appreciating yourself as you are right now.

Whilst writing this book, I have been reflecting on what age we start this negative campaign against ourselves and why so many of us struggle to see our worth. I wonder, were you taught to love yourself as a child, or did you grow up thinking that being self-critical and not liking yourself is normal? Was it seen as big-headed to think highly of oneself? You may recall phrases like, "Look at him; he loves himself!" Or, "Who does she think she is wearing that outfit?" Growing up, I learnt that thinking too much of yourself was frowned upon. No one actually said this; it was just what I learnt from others' comments and behaviours. If you received this message, you might have developed the belief that it is not okay to love yourself.

You may have grown up listening to other family members berating themselves. "Oh, you should have seen the state of me in my swimsuit, I looked like a beached whale!" Or, "My belly is huge, anyone would think I am pregnant!" As children, we always look for clues about how to behave as adults. The clue offered here is that we should be very self-critical and tell everyone how disgusted we are with ourselves! (Bonus tip: be mindful of how you talk about yourself in front of children, they are always listening!)

I have several memories of schoolgirls asking me, "Who do you think you are?" As a thirteen-year-old, being asked this question surrounded by a gang is soul-destroying. I interpreted it as, "Do you think you are better than me?" ("If so, I will hurt you!") The message I received was to stay hidden, don't like yourself, and you will be safe. So, I learnt that life would be easier in many ways if I did just that.

So why is self-love important when it comes to what we eat? Well, if we love ourselves, we are more likely to take better care of ourselves, including what we eat. Consider your love for others, whether a child, partner or close friend. You praise them for doing well; you show your love and appreciation. You want them to be successful in whatever they do. When we love and value someone, we take care of them. The same goes for our possessions. Think about how you look after your jewellery, car, home items and clothes. If you have bought a stylish, high-end winter coat, you look after it. You keep it in the wardrobe rather than in the cupboard under the stairs. You take it to be dry cleaned.

So why is self-love important when it comes to what we eat? Well, if we love ourselves, we are more likely to take better care of ourselves, including what we eat.

You love and value the coat, so you look after it. Self-love is connected to your self-worth. If you do not value and respect yourself, you will not love yourself. Various factors can affect our self-worth. If someone has been unkind to you at work, this may have an impact on how you feel about yourself and lower your self-worth. Equally, when you receive praise, it can have a positive impact on raising your self-worth. As you improve your self-worth and work on your thoughts, feelings and beliefs (more on this later), you will be able to regulate this easier and stay in a place of high self-worth.

Several signs indicate low self-worth, including negative self-talk, people-pleasing and avoiding new opportunities because you believe you will fail. Difficulty accepting compliments, perfectionism, difficulty setting boundaries because you don't believe you are worthy of a person's respect or believe others' needs are more important than yours. Then, constantly comparing yourself to others and feeling like you fall short, doubting your abilities and judgement.

Before we dive into the activities, I wanted to speak to the mums, grandparents and carers out there. It is common to put your child's needs before your own. I have done it myself. I've made Nancy's lunch and picked at her leftovers because I didn't consider my needs. I have used Nancy as an excuse not to work out, go swimming or go for a walk. Then I gained a new perspective. Think about it this way: if you have children, grandchildren, nieces or nephews, what beliefs do you want to instil in them? Do you want them to know that looking after themselves should be a priority? That even when they become a parent, their needs are essential too? Or do you want them to think that once you become a mum, you are destined for a life of running around after everyone else? I have no memories of my parents taking care of themselves, which is why it is not naturally part of who I am. So, how about we show future generations that self-love is the best love? Plus, you need to remember (and this is one of my favourite sayings) you can't pour from an empty cup! If you constantly pour your energy into everyone else but you never fill your own cup, it will become dry. By making sure your own needs are met too, you will have more to give to others.

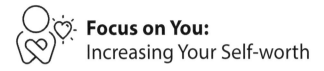

Focus on You:
Increasing Your Self-worth

To increase your self-worth and self-esteem, you need to show yourself some love, respect and appreciation. Then, hopefully, you will want to take better care of yourself! Not only with the food you eat but the situations you put yourself in, the content you read and watch, and the people you spend time with.

Below are some simple ways to increase your self-worth. You may wish to choose a couple to focus on each week going forward until you have mastered them all.

1. Challenge negative self-talk: work on catching yourself engaging in negative self-talk and try to counter these thoughts with reminders of your strengths and accomplishments.

You can't pour from an empty cup.

2. Focus on your strengths: make a list of your strengths, skills and positive qualities, and remind yourself of them regularly.

3. Practise self-care: take care of yourself physically, emotionally and mentally. Engage in activities that bring you joy and make you feel good about yourself.

4. Surround yourself with positive people: build a tribe of supportive friends and family members who uplift and encourage you. We will cover this more in chapter eleven.

5. Set realistic goals: setting and achieving goals can boost self-esteem, but it's important to set achievable goals that are realistic and aligned with your values. We will cover this in chapter ten.

6. Practise gratitude: focus on what you have rather than what you don't have. What made you smile today? What are you grateful for? Express appreciation for the positive things in your life and the people who support you.

7. Ensure you are getting plenty of rest, whether that is sleep or just downtime.

8. Schedule in time to do things you want, especially if you never have time because you are doing things for others.

Remember, improving your self-worth is a process that may take time, but with practice, you can learn to value yourself for the amazing, unique person you are.

Focus on You:
Love Letter

Writing a letter to yourself can feel strange, but it is super powerful! Years ago, I had a client who started writing love letters to herself as a simple way to show herself appreciation. Every weekend, she would not only write a letter but post it too! She would express her gratitude for her excellent work, remind herself of her achievements and marvel at what a wonderful human she was! Imagine opening that letter on a rainy Monday morning, what a way to start a week!

So, I challenge you to give this a go. Write the letter as if you were writing it to your best friend. I want you to pour your appreciation and love into this letter. Focus on how incredible you are. I appreciate no one may have told you this before, and I know you may not have told yourself this in a long time, if ever, so now is your opportunity.

The questions and thoughts below will help you formulate your letter. You do not need to use all of them, just take what resonates with you and leave the rest.

1. What is a quality within you (not appearance) that you like or love about yourself? It may be your sense of humour, your willingness to learn new information, that you are great at communication or that you are a good friend.
2. What have you achieved that you are proud of?

54

Maybe something you never thought you would do, but you did! This could be gaining a degree, being promoted, climbing a mountain, raising a child, running a business, caring for a loved one.

3. Now focus on your amazing body. If your inner self says it is not amazing, be open to a discussion with her. What can your body do? It could be walking your child to school. Maybe it takes you on a shopping trip or to the theatre. It may allow you to dance with your friends or walk you around London. Maybe your body has survived illness, a pandemic, maybe it has grown a child or several!

4. What about your mind? It allows you to read, think and develop your skills. Has your mind survived trauma, a complicated relationship, or losing a loved one?

Let yourself explore you, not the physical you but the real authentic, unique you.

Below is an example of one of my client's love letters (shared with her permission):

Dear Kate,

Please forgive the letter format; I am not ready to say these words out loud (yet). I will be one day. I am working on loving you and aim to look you in the eye one day and say I love you. I hope this day is not far away.

I know that you know how difficult this journey is for me, but I am determined, strong and I will do this.

I want you to know that I am in awe of everything you have been through, and I am proud of your achievements. You're a fantastic mummy. You are kind and patient and work hard to give Elsie the best life ever, no matter what else is going on around you. You are single-handedly raising a beautiful little girl, and you work hard not to pass on your issues with food. (Even if it kills you to scrape half of her dinner in the bin!)

You are brilliant at your job. I know you don't like to admit it and don't accept the praise, but you have been promoted several times, and you are the go-to person for help within the office. I know you don't know everything and criticise yourself for that, but maybe it is time to accept that you will never know everything!

As for your body, I understand that many factors have brought you to where you are now. This is not your fault. You have coped with life the best you could, and sometimes that has meant using food to soothe and to pick you up. This is okay; we will work on this together. But let's just focus on how amazing your body is. It has walked for twelve hours around Disneyland for six days, sometimes carrying Elsie. I know this was a real challenge, but you did it. Each day you push yourself to walk to school even when it would be easier to drive. You do your best to keep moving despite the pain and embarrassment you constantly feel.

I want you to know I am here to help you, and I want to work together. I want to work on this food stuff once and for all.

Kate, I do love you. I just lost my way, and writing this letter has helped me to see that.

All my love, Kate x

CHAPTER 6

Understanding You

I have met hundreds of women starting their journey from a place of anger, fear or frustration (often all three). Angry and frustrated with themselves. In their words, they 'allowed' themselves to get to this place, angry and frustrated with partners for their lack of understanding and support, angry with past weight loss groups that failed them, and angry with food because it tastes so good! Then there is the fear of trying again and not succeeding, especially when it feels like the world is watching, waiting for this to happen. In this chapter, I encourage you to acknowledge where you are right now, accept it and then forgive all that has passed.

Mary's Story

Mary was sixty-seven, and one of my first group members back in 2005. She had been dieting since the birth of her first child when she was twenty-five. As I opened the first session and shared a little about who I was and my weight loss journey, I felt a cold reception from Mary. When I asked if there were any immediate questions, Mary said in an off tone, "So, do you just eat salad now?" I took this to mean, "Are you going to tell me to live on salad?" I replied as honestly as I could. "No, I eat a varied diet, I eat all foods, and occasionally I even choose cake over lunch, but I am okay with that. I am still working on my own relationship with food, but I can honestly say I am in a peaceful place with it compared to five years ago." Mary let out a 'huh' and raised her eyebrows. I knew I needed to gain her trust if she was going to stick with the programme.

I gently asked the group to share their biggest fear or worry about embarking on the programme. One by one, they shared the same fear, the fear of failure. Mary said she was worried about wasting more money on herself because she had spent thousands of pounds on dieting and believed she was a lost cause. I nodded to acknowledge Mary's words and asked her if she really believed that. She stayed quiet, and after a minute or so, I suggested that somewhere inside, a small part of Mary thought she could have a healthier relationship with food. That part of her brought her to this group and enrolled her in a twelve-week programme. Mary nodded and then shared that she desperately wanted it, but she was too scared to believe it would work in case it didn't.

In later weeks, Mary shared her story. Through our group work, she recognised where food became more than a source of energy. Mary's first husband became abusive when she was pregnant. Along with other hurtful and damaging comments, he had told her she was a 'lost cause'. Mary had struggled in the early weeks of motherhood; her daughter didn't feed or settle easily. She quickly became overwhelmed and exhausted, and food became her go-to. She had felt so alone. She remembered thinking that if she was a lost cause, it didn't matter what she ate.

Mary was angry with herself. She said she wished she had been *stronger and stood up to her ex-husband years earlier than she did. She noticed she would still overindulge when she felt alone or scared. Even though she had a comfortable life and a loving husband, the old wounds had not healed; they needed to be acknowledged and released. Mary now recognises when she is feeling lonely or scared; she has strategies in place, such as speaking to her husband or friend. She also knows these feelings will pass and that eating will not make this happen any quicker.*

Like Mary, you will have your own story, the path you have taken this far that has led you to where you are now with food. Whether triggered by events in your life or just a combination of habits you have developed, it is time to let them go. I also invite you to see the years of dieting not as failed attempts but as an opportunity to learn (more on this later). You are where you are, and as no one has invented time travel, you can't go back, you can only go forward. With this in mind, there is no point wasting time on regrets, wishing you had loved your body at sixteen when you thought you were fat. Or berating yourself for not keeping your weight off twenty years ago when you lost it for your wedding or dream holiday. There is no mileage in blaming your parents for the large portions, the grandparents for their sugary treats, and the partners, past and present, for the cosy nights indulging in takeaways. I know these people have all played their part in how you have developed your eating habits, but let's park that for now. We will explore relationships later in this book.

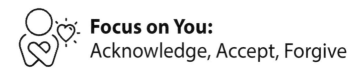 **Focus on You:**
Acknowledge, Accept, Forgive

Let's take a moment to check in with your past and any areas you may need to work on letting go. After grounding yourself with some slow breathing, I invite you to answer the following questions. Again, you will be connecting with yourself on a deeper level, allow your thoughts to come through and allow yourself time to sit with your emotions.

I acknowledge:
(What do you wish to acknowledge? This may be something in the past or it is recognising and validating how you feel right now.)

I accept:
(What do you wish to accept?)

I forgive:
(Who or what do you wish to forgive?)

I am ready to let go of:
(What are you ready to let go of? This may be thoughts, beliefs or feelings or something else.)

Moving forward, I promise:
(Would you like to make some promises to yourself? I would love you to write promises, maybe a commitment to working through this book, a pledge

of respecting or loving yourself, or a promise of developing a deeper understanding of yourself.)

Building Awareness

Life flows easier when you give yourself the time and space to make sense of the thoughts in your head. With this in mind, I encourage you to build awareness around your relationship with yourself, others and food. Think – you cannot change what you cannot see. I want you to step back from what you already know and GET CURIOUS about YOU! Journaling is highly recommended for emotional well-being. Writing down your thoughts and feelings helps you to understand them and gain clarity. See this as a brain-dumping exercise, getting your jumbled thoughts onto the page. As overeating is usually connected with our moods, being able to regulate our emotions is helpful. Your journal entries are not about logging your food; I want you to notice your thoughts and feelings.

I invite you to tune in to how you think and feel as you go through your week.

Who are you? What lights you up, brings you joy? What makes you feel uncomfortable, unhappy, stressed, anxious, frustrated? What areas of your life are you content with? What areas would you change? Is it just food that is the issue or is something else causing you discomfort? How, when and where did your current relationship with food develop? How has that affected your life? Has it had an impact on relationships, jobs and social occasions? And where are you

Life flows easier when you give yourself the time and space to make sense of the thoughts in your head.

now? These are great questions for you to ponder. Later, I will share some daily prompts.

If your inner voice is shouting, "No, I hate journaling!" then great! Let's explore that first.

Maybe she is not comfortable or ready to think about her relationship with food or maybe she thinks there is no point. If you are having these thoughts, brilliant! It is your inner self trying to keep you safe and at your set point. Whenever you do anything out of your comfort zone, you will hear her. Just remind her that she is safe, promise her you will take this slow and steady, and we will work with her more in a moment. It is entirely normal to feel resistance here. In fact, over the years, I have lost count of the times my clients have said to me, "I just can't write things down," or, "I just stare at the page." Many of us have never processed our day in this way, so it is easy to understand why we find it challenging. There may be the fear of getting it wrong or the worry that someone will read it, and then there is the fear of what you may write. Maybe you know deep down what you would write, but you have shoved that so far down that you are using food to keep it there.

Jane's Story

Jane was fifty-three when we started working together, with a loving husband, a grown-up daughter who was expecting her first child and, in Jane's words, she had a perfect life. She told me her only problem was food. She told me how she just couldn't control herself.

When I first met Jane, I asked her if she would be open to keeping a diary. She squirmed uncomfortably but said she would give it a go. I asked Jane, "Where is the resistance?" She said she would prefer not to write things down and didn't want her husband to read it. I asked her if she would be willing to answer three questions each day, whether via a voice memo, notes on her phone, or in a physical diary. Jane said, "I'll try," which often means, 'I probably won't'! The thing is, "I'll try," permits you not to. It is non-committal.

The following week, Jane wrote in her journal twice. She said she didn't think it helped her and didn't think there was any point writing going forward. I gently asked her again, "Where is the resistance?" Jane said she felt stupid talking about her feelings and wasn't sure that working with me would work for her. I gently asked why she felt stupid talking about her feelings. She stared at her feet, then said, "We don't do that." I nodded and asked, "May I ask who you are referring to when you say 'we'?" Jane took a big breath and said, "My family, we don't talk about our feelings. We just get on with things." Jane was doing everything she could to hold back the tears. I held the space for her to process what she had said. I then said, "Jane, do you think this works for you? Not talking about your feelings? Just getting on with things?" Jane quickly said, "Yes, it has worked so far." I nodded. "Has it?" I said. "Has it really worked for you?" Jane looked at me with realisation in her eyes. "I have just suppressed my feelings with food, haven't I?"

At that moment, Jane let her emotions flood out. She told me how burying her feelings had affected her whole life, trying to make sense of everything internally because that is how she had been taught to deal with life. It often caused tension in her relationship because she could not open up. Jane admitted she had been using food for over thirty years to relieve uncomfortable feelings. For Jane, this was a turning point; she had finally begun to release years of trapped pain.

Jane began to develop a deeper understanding of herself. She learnt to process her thoughts and feelings and no longer needed to bury her feelings with food. I asked her if I could share her story and if she had one thing she would say to my readers. Her answer was, "Trust the process. If you are like me, you will want to fight it, but the answers lie in doing the inner work, not the diet."

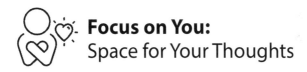 **Focus on You:**
Space for Your Thoughts

There are countless journals available online and on the high street these days, but I still haven't found one that encompasses everything I would want to write about each day. Yes, creating a well-being journal is on my to-do list! Sometimes it is helpful to just let your words flow and notice what thoughts splash out onto your paper. In other circumstances, you may prefer some simple questions to help guide you. Below are the questions I use myself and with my clients. I recommend you glance over the list and pick those that feel relevant to you each day. You may wish to pop them on a Post-it note and move them through your notebook as you write, choosing three-to-five questions each day. Remember to journal without judgement.

How was yesterday?
- What went well?
- What could I have done differently? (This is a general question about your day, not necessarily about food.)

What are my plans for the day ahead?
- How do I feel about today?
- What support might I need? (This is a general question about your day, not necessarily about food.)

How can I nourish my mind and body today?
- Do I have a clear plan?
- Are there any challenges in my way? (Think about food, movement and your mindset.)

List three things you are grateful for
(Practising gratitude daily elevates your mood and energy levels.)

CHAPTER 7

The Scales and You

Those with a love/hate relationship with food often have an unhealthy obsession with how much their body weighs. For many, watching the scales go up and down is a bigger part of their life than they ever wanted it to be. In this chapter, I will remind you how scales can affect your progress but, more importantly, your mental health. I will share examples from my career in dieting. Then I will share healthy ways to track your progress. I do not doubt that you already know what you will read in the following pages. However, I hope these thoughts will help you decide whether to continue your relationship with the scales or initiate a break-up! Whilst it is natural to want to track your progress, if the number on the scales doesn't match what you'd hoped for, it can lead to feelings of disappointment, frustration, confusion and sometimes even guilt, shame and self-hatred. If you don't have an attachment to your weight, I am doing a happy dance for you! Congratulations on not being tied to the numbers in the box. On the other hand, if you find yourself preoccupied with hopping on and off, and moving the scales to another room to see if your weight is any different, then it is time to

If you don't have an attachment to your weight, I am doing a happy dance for you!

consider whether weighing is for you.

Whilst working in the dieting industry, I lost count of the times I witnessed the following scene play out. My client would bounce into their weekly meeting, saying, "I feel amazing, I am making great choices, I think I am finally listening to my body, and I know I have lost weight." They were on cloud nine. But then, the reading on the scales did not match their expectations. Their jaw dropped. They got off and on a few times before slumping into the chair in despair. The hope of a 'good loss' was destroyed once again. Then their inner investigator stepped in as they dissected their food choices over the past seven days. *Maybe I should have eaten less fruit. What if the meal I had in that restaurant was cooked in fat? Was it the two chocolates I ate at work? I knew I shouldn't have tried that mouthful of my son's school cooking project.* My clients were very well-educated on how their weight can fluctuate, as I am sure you are. We all know that water retention due to various factors including hormone changes and inflammation can cause weight gain. The contents of our stomach and whether we have recently been to the bathroom can also change our weight. And there can be temporary fluctuations from physical activity and some medications. However, at this moment, my client's brain had eliminated this information in a desperate attempt to find an answer so they did not make the same mistake the following week. Despite our extended discussion on the subject, I knew they were leaving the room with a low mood and a pile of unhelpful thoughts, ranging from, "What's the point? I may as well have a takeaway tonight," to, "I need to eat even less next week to ensure this doesn't happen again." Sometimes they could work through this; sometimes, their thoughts would spiral, having an impact on their food choices, and they would allow the emotion to affect their food choices for days, sometimes weeks.

Alice's Story

Alice's meal replacement plan to lose three stone worked well, but her dream of staying at nine stone was too challenging, and her body wanted to settle slightly higher. In an attempt to keep her weight down, Alice developed a habit of restricting her food intake to very few calories. She had also developed a habit of daily weighing. Alice told me she liked to feel in control of food and her weight and was happier when she ate small portions. Alice was in a cycle of eating very little for days, and then when something triggered her, usually something happening in her life that was beyond her control, she would binge on chocolate. Alice's intake was so low that her body was crying out for nourishment. The more she restricted her food, the greater her urge to eat. Alice blamed life's circumstances each time she caved in, and whilst they may have been a trigger, the reality was her body was desperate for fuel.

Alice was on a mission to be nine stone. Nine stone two pounds was her closest but never nine stone. I asked Alice to consider why it was so important to her to be that weight. At first, she wasn't sure. She said, "I just know I will be happy there." I invited her to explore this. Alice recalled a boy she dated in her early twenties. He had told her she was fat. Alice was ten stone at the time. Alice remembered feeling crushed and completely deflated. She left the house that evening to meet him, feeling confident and secure in herself but returned as someone who questioned her weight, size and food choices. Alice had internalised this as: "If I am over nine stone, I am not attractive. If I can reach nine stone, I will be lovable."

Through our work together, we talked about her other relationships and how she had compounded the belief that she needed to be nine stone to be attractive and loved. "If I am nine stone, I will find a man who loves me and treats me well."

Alice said she didn't want to be in a serious relationship, she wouldn't want to live with anyone again, and she was happy on her own with her huge circle of friends. Was Alice sabotaging herself to stay in a place she deemed unlovable so that she didn't find a partner? Was this her way of staying safe and single? When she recognised this, it was her first step to healing her relationship with food. As we got to work on raising her self-esteem, Alice decided not to weigh herself for a month – which was a huge step. Within a couple of weeks, Alice noticed that her food choices improved because she ate from a place of curiosity and finally listened to her body. She wasn't eating to manage the numbers and she was no longer in the restrict/binge cycle. Alice was finally free! There were moments over the coming months when she drifted back to her old safety net of knowing the numbers, but eventually, Alice decided to throw her scales away!

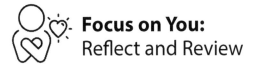 **Focus on You:**
Reflect and Review

I invite you to step back and think about the logical use of measuring, from distance to volume, speed to temperature. We weigh ingredients to ensure our cake has a perfect balance of sugar, flour and butter.

Your fuel gauge – or these days, battery charge indicator – tells us how far you can travel with the energy you have in the tank or battery. And your watch tells you the time you have to read this book before going to sleep, work or whatever you are doing next. Then there's the bathroom scales; they measure your weight, not your self-worth, not your awesomeness, your weight! For some, weighing regularly is helpful, and tracking progress keeps them motivated. For others, the ritual of stepping on the scales is extremely counterproductive and can be a trigger for overeating. Logically, you know scales do not measure your worth. But just like my clients, the logic can go out the window in any given moment!

So, I guess my question is, do you want to let go of the scales? Would your mind be calmer and more settled if you didn't weigh? I know it can feel scary, and the concern may be, *If I don't weigh, I will gain weight*, BUT, if you are using other methods (such as those in this book) to work on your relationship with food, then you know you are making changes, and that means you will be making progress. You don't need those numbers to tell you. You may choose to measure your progress by how you feel, how many times you ate consciously or how many times you chose to move your body. If you still need some sort of physical measure, you could use a tape measure and take down your bust, hips, waist, arms and leg measurements. If completely letting go of the scales still feels challenging, you may choose to weigh less often – fortnightly or monthly – and evaluate as you go.

The other option is to weigh daily. Okay, I know I am backtracking, but hear me out! Weighing daily allows you to see the fluctuations within your body and get used to the scales going up and down. I know some trainers who ask their clients to weigh daily and take the lowest weight of the week as their marker. This option is definitely not for everyone but works for some.

To summarise, I invite you to reflect on your feelings about the scales and whether you want to use them. Would you find it easier to heal your relationship with yourself and food without weighing? There is no right or wrong answer. The trick is knowing when weighing is valuable and when it is hindering you. Again, it's about understanding you.

CHAPTER 8

Limiting Beliefs and You

For years, I was the overweight girl who couldn't control herself. I couldn't stick to a diet for longer than a month. I hated exercise and had resigned myself to my endless battle with food and weight. Whilst these thoughts dominated my thinking, it is no surprise I struggled for so long. The thing is, we all have a story that we tell ourselves. It isn't necessarily true. It may have some factual information weaved in, but often it's embellished with crooked thinking and limiting beliefs. What is your story? What do you tell yourself about your body, your relationship with food and weight loss? In fact, what do you tell yourself about all areas of your life? How successful will you be, how much money can you earn, how lovable are you and what type of life are you destined to have? Do you hold the belief that possessing a larger body equates to being unattractive or lazy or that you lack self-control? (These are the thoughts that drive our ongoing struggle with food.)

Whatever your beliefs, it is important to recognise how they have an impact on your life. If the majority of your thoughts are helpful and balanced, you will be well-

What is your story? What do you tell yourself about your body, your relationship with food and weight loss?

equipped to manage not only your relationship with food but life in general. However, if you feed yourself with negative skewed thinking, then it is time for radical action. Think of a dripping tap leaking contaminated thoughts. Slowly flooding your mind with self-doubt and criticism. As Kristen Helmstetter says in *Coffee Self-Talk*[9], negative self-talk is like death from a thousand cuts; it doesn't slay you in a single negative instance or thought but you slowly die a little more with each harmful utterance. I want you to be able to change these beliefs and thoughts that are holding you back, whether about your body, food or anything else! Once you uncover the beliefs that are not serving you, you can set the intention to let them go.

Let's start with some examples. Have you ever told yourself...

"I will never lose weight."

"I always fail at diets."

"I am greedy."

"I can't control myself."

"I am big-boned."

"It's in my genes."

"People like me aren't meant to succeed."

"People judge me because of my body size."

"I am not good enough."

"I don't deserve to be happy."

"I can't have it all."

These are all limiting beliefs, things you tell yourself that stop you from achieving your goals. They affect your thoughts and actions around food. If your belief is, "I will never lose weight," it is unlikely that you will. The belief will have an impact on your eating habits and exercise routines because you believe no matter what you do, it will not make a difference. When you do get a burst of motivation, the change is short-lived because your subconscious mind is waiting to remind you that you will likely fail. Like telling you, *you have blown it* as soon as you have a square of chocolate or a glass of wine. Cue the barrage of unhelpful thoughts: *You know you will never lose weight! You may as well give up now! When will you accept you will always be this size?* And then you do the one thing that feels like it will offer some comfort, yet it is the one thing you are trying not to do. You eat.

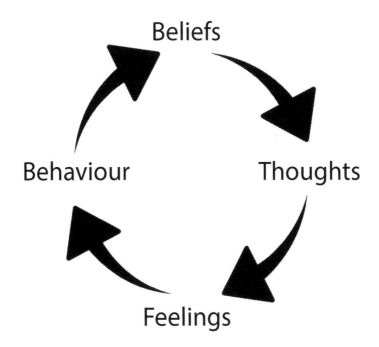

This pattern plays out in an endless cycle many of us stay stuck in for years. Unless you consciously change something, it will continue to steer the direction of your relationship with food. The good news is you can choose to step out of the cycle at any point. You can work on changing your beliefs, which we will come to in a moment. However, sometimes taking action is just as empowering. Imagine if you started acting like you already have a peaceful relationship with food? If you began to choose food each day that nourished your body? If you respected your body and told yourself how much you love it each day? How different would you feel in thirty days? It can be challenging to take that action if our beliefs tell us otherwise. This is why it is essential to find them and let them go.

Lindsey's Story

My client Lindsey had been on more diets than she could remember, often losing between two and three stone, putting it back on each time. When I started working with Lindsey, I asked her, "Do you believe you can lose weight?" Lindsey thought for a moment. "No," she said, then followed with, "I know I will never be able to lose it forever. I always put it back on." This belief affected her ability to reach her goal. It led to skipping meals to save calories, high-calorie snacking and torturing herself with starvation diets. It didn't matter what methods Lindsey tried because her view of herself was that she would always return to her old weight. I asked Lindsey if she thought her belief was entirely accurate and that she would always struggle, to which she replied, "Yes, that is just how I am." I explained to Lindsey that this belief was keeping her stuck, and whilst she held this belief, she would constantly battle between herself and food. "Would you ever consider you have become extremely skilled at weight loss? You have more than proved you can lose weight successfully on many occasions." She gave me half a smile and nodded at this realisation. The number of times she had lost weight flashed through her mind. I suggested Lindsey choose a new belief, and she decided on, "I am working on my relationship with food and myself." This new perspective became Lindsey's power and enabled her to move forward from a logical and relaxed place.

'I am not worthy' is another deep-rooted belief that many of my clients hold. 'I am not worthy of loving myself', 'I am not worthy of living in a body I love', 'I am not worthy of a promotion', 'I am not worthy of meeting a partner'. Remember, we are not always aware of the beliefs we hold. A hidden belief may be, 'it is not safe to lose weight'. Sometimes women can feel invisible in a larger body. Shrinking can attract unwanted attention, so staying where they are can subconsciously feel safe. I have worked with many ladies ready to meet their life partners; they wanted to lose weight as they thought they would feel more confident dating. Despite self-love being their primary key to unlocking confidence, their belief was, "I will be lovable when I lose weight." However, the underlying fear was, "What if I lose weight and I don't find love? What if I am still unlovable?" Can you see why it may feel safer not to make the change?

At three years old, I was admitted into hospital with bronchitis. I remember being carried into the ambulance. In those days, parents didn't stay with their children overnight. Being away from my family was very unsettling, and I would wait for my mummy and daddy to visit me each day. I recall lots of talk about how 'thin' I was. I was underweight for my age. The doctors and my parents were concerned, so I was encouraged to eat and praised for finishing food. When I was well enough to return home, the praise continued, along with, "You need to keep your strength up!" My subconscious mind learnt that eating and gaining weight would keep me safe and healthy, and I would not have to go back to the hospital. I didn't uncover this belief until I was in my late twenties.

Where Do Our Beliefs Come From?

Many of our beliefs are created at an early age. Growing up, our minds work hard to make sense of the world. As we take in information from those around us, we form thoughts about ourselves, others and the world in general. By observing our family, friends, teachers, environment and experiences, our brain forms what essentially are energy-saving shortcuts. Our parents or caregivers are our first teachers. Their comments and discussions around food, body image, other people, work, money and life in general shape how we view the world. You may have heard the women in your family say they look awful in their swimsuits or that their stomach stuck out in their dresses. Or heard typical diet talk about being good and bad, cheat days and how many pounds they had lost or gained.

You may have received messages about clearing your plate, not wasting food and it even being rude to refuse food. Some of these thoughts have been passed through the generations.

Your grandparents may have lived through times of food being scarce. Hence the saying 'you have to clear your plate' or 'you must not waste food'. They knew nothing else was in the cupboard, so they would ensure their children ate the available food. Telling others not to waste food back then was necessary. Nowadays food is usually available and often in abundance, so this message is outdated.

Aside from beliefs about food, you also have beliefs in other areas of your life, for example, beliefs about other people, beliefs about how we should behave and what is socially acceptable, and beliefs about money and work ethics. These are again shaped by those around you and affect how we operate in the world. A huge one for me was money beliefs. Growing up, both of my parents were self-employed. My dad a heating and plumbing engineer, and my mum a hairstylist. They worked long hours and owned a hairdressing shop where we also lived. My mum would often go back to the salon to mop the floor at 11pm, or start work early to squeeze a client in. My dad was sometimes on call through the night. It is funny the assumptions people make; it seemed that in our community, they were classed as millionaires because they owned a business! Others do not see the struggles, the graft or the money concerns when business was slow. I recall others saying to me and to them, "It is all right for you, you have money," and, "You can afford what you want!" I remember my mum and dad feeling hurt and frustrated by these comments. Here they were, working till all hours to pay for family holidays and give us a better life than they had whilst others were making remarks about how easy they had it. For years I believed that people didn't like you if you had money.

I hated discussing money, and I would never ask the salary in a job interview. I even used to feel uncomfortable charging for my services and often gave way too much of my time for free because I didn't want to be judged if I asked for payment. Having this belief didn't pay the bills, that's for sure!

Can I take a moment to say I don't blame my parents or anyone else for my beliefs, whether around food, money or anything else. We are all doing our best to navigate our way through life with the information available to us, both internally and externally. We are not taught this in school. In fact, unless you read self-development books or work on your own growth, then it is unlikely that you have worked on your beliefs before today. Whilst you may not have consciously created your beliefs, they are yours and only you can change them. If you want to experience different outcomes, you must learn how to change your current programming. As you explore your beliefs, please take care of yourself. You may uncover emotions and thoughts that you have hidden from yourself. Ensure you surround yourself with loved ones. If it helps to talk through your findings, confide in a close friend or family member or seek professional support.

Are you ready to choose a new story?

Focus on You:
Changing Your Beliefs

Step 1: Identify your current beliefs
Take a moment to jot down all your thoughts and beliefs about food, your weight and your body. Do

you believe you can lose weight? Or is your belief 'I will always be this size'? Do you tell yourself, "I am addicted to food"? Have you convinced yourself, "I am not worthy of losing weight," or, "I am greedy"? What are your thoughts as you read this book? Have you already decided, *It won't work for me*? You may also want to reflect on where these beliefs come from and make a note of this too. (See example below.)

Step 2: Think of moments in your life that contradict your beliefs

This is where we are collecting evidence to say the belief is not true. In fact, it is utter rubbish! So, for example, let's say your belief is 'I am greedy'. If you take time to reflect, are you greedy in every situation or do you sometimes leave food on your plate, refuse dessert or happily not touch food in the cupboard?

Current belief and where it has come from	Evidence to say the belief is not true
I am greedy.	I sometimes leave food.
I remember others saying this about me at a Christmas party when I went back to the buffet as a child.	I often refuse dessert. I can happily leave food in the cupboard.

I will never lose weight. Years of trying to lose weight then regaining it. The rest of my family struggles, so I believe I will too.	I have lost weight countless times. There is also nothing wrong with being this weight.
I am unlovable if I am in a larger body.	I have a close circle of people who love me. We are all different and have unique qualities that make us lovable. Size is irrelevant.

Step 3: Create your new empowered beliefs

It is time to reprogramme your thought patterns so that they support you. This isn't about positive thinking, it's about logical, balanced thinking. So, instead of, 'I am greedy', you may choose something like, 'I enjoy eating to nourish my body'.

Current Belief	Empowered Belief
I am greedy.	I enjoy eating to nourish my body.
I will never lose weight.	I am learning how to have a healthier relationship with food.
I am unlovable if I am in a larger body.	I am working on loving me for who I am not my size.

LIMITING BELIEFS AND YOU

Step 4: Embody the new beliefs

Each day write down your new beliefs and then visualise yourself as if you already have these beliefs, notice how differently you act around food, how different you feel. Spending a couple of minutes each day imagining the version of you that has fully downloaded these new beliefs can really help you to embrace this change.

I will share a little more on the power of visualisation in the following chapter.

Step 5: Thank and move on

In the early days, you are bound to hear that old script creeping in, trying to pull you back to your old programming. As Holly Matthews says in her best-selling book, *The Happy Me Project*[10], beware of ANTS (automatic negative thoughts)!

When you hear these, thank them and move on.

You may even choose to say out loud, "Ah, there you are! Thank you for reminding me of my old beliefs; however, I am choosing to live by (insert new belief) today!"

Step 6: Food freedom affirmations

Affirmations are statements you say to yourself each day to help embed your new beliefs. It may be simply repeating your belief, 'I enjoy eating to nourish my body', over and over whilst you are in the shower, preparing food, driving or out walking. Using regular affirmations will help shape your new ways of thinking, improve your mood and reprogramme your subconscious mind. More on this in the next chapter.

CHAPTER 9

Aligning You

When I started writing this book, I had developed a keen interest in energy alignment and decided to study several modalities so that I could share them with my clients. It has now become a huge part of my world, so I decided to add this chapter in after I had written the first draft. Being able to align your energy will support you with your food freedom goals. We can all recall moments when we have been fully focused and tuned in to nourishing our body. Those times when you are immersed in what you need to do; your head is in the game, so to speak. Everything is always easier when we find this energy and drive. If only we could bottle this feeling! Okay. Maybe we can't bottle it, but we can create it. We can align our energy to be on the same frequency as the person we are evolving into. We can create the feeling of being in the game, and it is not as difficult as you may think!

The law of attraction theory has become more widespread in recent years, particularly with best-selling books such as *The Secret* by Rhonda Byrne[11] and *Manifest* by Roxie Nafousi[12]. I know you will have heard the phrase 'law of attraction', but have you ever given it much thought? Maybe you already use it in some areas of your life. Whether you are a firm believer in the law of attraction or not, this chapter is aimed to help you understand how to raise your vibration so that you are operating on the frequency of optimum health and weight loss!

If you have read *The Secret* by Rhonda Byrne, you may know the phrase, 'our thoughts create our reality'. In other words, if we think about something enough, it eventually comes true. I know what you are thinking; I have thought about losing weight for half my life, which has never come true! Or, I have dreamed about winning the lottery, but I am still waiting!

The thing is, whilst, in essence, our thoughts create our reality, there are a few more steps to the law of attraction process. *The Secret* states that we can have anything in three simple steps:

Step 1: We ask the universe for it.

Step 2: We believe we can have it.

Step 3: We receive it.

I appreciate that sounds very hard to believe, and I will admit there is a little more to it than the three steps. But let's just take a look at the steps, especially step two, as it is the biggie! Do you genuinely believe you can crack this food stuff or even win big on the lottery? For most, the answer will be no. Or, "Yes I can, but I know I will regain my weight at some point." So, the belief is 'I always regain the weight I lose'. So, if that is your belief, that is what you receive (step three). And as we discussed in the previous chapter, you will find it an uphill struggle until you change your beliefs about your relationship with food.

I read *The Secret* around fifteen years ago, and it ma
so much sense that I started recommending it to all my
clients. More recently, I discovered the real power of
energy alignment and how, when properly understood, it
can be used to radically change your life. Understanding
and managing your energy is the single, most important
thing you can do for yourself. Various energy modalities
exist, but a friend introduced me to The Helix Method®[13].
This energy psychology practice blew my mind! Let me
share how the most wonderful human taught me this, my
incredible mentor and the founder of The Helix Method®,
Louisa Havers[14].

First, we know everything is energy, and everything has
a frequency and vibration. We are all familiar with devices in
our homes that operate on a frequency; microwaves, radios,
mobile phones and, of course, wi-fi. We also know that by
changing the frequency, we can change the outcome. So, if we
change the dial on the radio, we tune into a different station. If
we change the TV channel, we receive another programme on
our screen. Humans are no different; we operate on various
waves and frequencies. Throughout the day, you are sending
out signals into the world. Sometimes you give out a signal
that you are happy, thriving and that life is easy! And on these
days, you will find that your days flow easily. On other days,
your frequency is lower. You send out a completely different
message. It may be that life is hard, or 'I will never lose weight;
I like high-calorie food too much'. When you give out these
messages, you get the same back; the universe hears 'life is
hard', and so it gives you hard! The universe hears, 'I always
want high-calorie food', so you crave high-calorie food!

Sometimes you give out a signal that life is easy! On other days, your frequency is 'I will never lose weight.'

In The Helix Method®, we call it your human wi-fi. Your human wi-fi is your aura, your energy field, and your memories, experiences, emotions, thoughts and beliefs are imprinted onto your energy field. Your thoughts and feelings control what you hold in your field and what you send out. This affects your daily life experience, environment, relationships, friendships, family, work, health and weight. Most of us can relate to being in a difficult place in life and our mind. A time when your world felt like it was misaligned, everywhere you turned there was another obstacle, and somehow you attracted more and more challenges. This was because you were operating on a low frequency. As you vibrated on that level, you attracted more low-vibe situations. Sometimes, we are taken down to a low frequency through life's circumstances, trauma and tragic events. But more often, we unconsciously choose to stay at a low frequency, stuck in the mundane life cycle. Most of the population coast through life at a low frequency, unaware of their ability to change or they simply don't believe they can.

Energy States

Alongside the frequency, we operate from three energy states. Receptive (or in flow), resistance and reversal. Ideally, we would always be receptive or in flow. An example of being in flow would be one of those days when everything is easy. You are ready for work before you need to be, which gives you time to tidy the kitchen. Work is easy, and your boss suggests you finish early, all traffic lights are on green, and you stop at the shop only to find a bargain! When we are in flow, we can work towards our goals with ease and speed. New opportunities seem to fall in our lap; eating nourishing foods and moving your body seems less of an effort; in fact, it feels easy!

When we are in resistance, it feels like we are taking a few steps forward, but you have heavy metal boots on. You know where you want to get to, but you can't seem to get there. Around food, you may set yourself a target, get started on your diet and then someone invites you to dinner at a pizza restaurant. Or you forget to take your lunch to work and only unhealthy options are left in the canteen. It is like the universe is throwing obstacles in the way!

Then we have reversal, which can feel like you are going backwards. Even though you want to lose weight, you eat high-calorie foods that do not serve you each day. As you eat, you know you don't even want it, but you continue to eat! Sometimes it is like you are watching this happen and don't know how to stop it.

So how do you change your frequency? How do you stay in flow? Don't worry. I am going to share some of the techniques we use from The Helix Method®, but first, I want you also to be aware of your levels of consciousness, your beliefs and your identity.

Levels of Consciousness

You may already be familiar with the iceberg of consciousness, but here is a quick reminder.

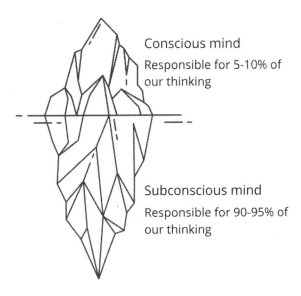

Conscious mind
Responsible for 5-10% of
our thinking

Subconscious mind
Responsible for 90-95% of
our thinking

So, you have your conscious mind; this is where you decide on your goals and where you plan to lose weight from. You think about the logical weight loss process and what you need to do to get from A to B. However, your conscious mind is unfortunately only responsible for five-to-ten percent of your thinking. Most of your thoughts happen out of awareness in your subconscious mind. Your subconscious mind is filled with your daily habits, values, beliefs and emotions. In other words, most of your thinking is done on autopilot. Super helpful in some ways, as we make around 35,000 decisions daily – that would be pretty hard going from your conscious mind (insert emoji with the exploding head!). We don't need to think about how we get ready each morning, whether to brush our teeth or make a cup of tea; we do these things instinctively. Unfortunately, not all our lifestyle habits

Your subconscious mind is filled with your daily habits, values, beliefs and emotions.

are helpful or healthy. The other thing to remember is the subconscious mind has an important job to do. It is there to keep you safe, just like your inner child. They are intrinsically linked. It wants to keep you where you are because it is familiar and it is your comfort zone. Remember, sometimes as you change, your subconscious mind finds reasons for you to quit and return to your default set point.

Then we have your higher self or superconscious. This is where your light-bulb moments come from, when you have great intuition or those gut feelings. Have you ever listened to your intuition when it felt like a wild idea, and taking action paid off? Or had a gut feeling about something or someone, but you tried to ignore it? The feeling comes back and presents itself differently until you listen. That right there is your superconscious speaking to you. My superconscious and other people told me to launch my coaching business in 2015, but I ignored it and opened a performing arts academy! I guess I wasn't quite ready to listen! When you are entirely in a flow state, and things are easy, your best ideas come through because you have a better connection to your superconscious. Then it is only your belief system that holds you back, just like mine did in 2015, telling me I was not good enough to offer my services without a known brand behind me.

Beliefs and Identity

As we covered beliefs in the last chapter, you have already started to work on your thoughts about yourself and your weight. Now I want you to think deeper than your beliefs. I want you to think about your identity because all the beliefs you hold make up your identity. Your identity is who you are right now, how you see yourself in this world, and how you expect your life to play out.

If your current identity is 'Sarah Version 1.0, who, no matter how hard she tries, will always battle with food', then you always will. You need to upgrade your identity. You must embrace a new version of yourself, the 2.0 version! The you who believes she has a healthy relationship food, believes she can release weight, believes in self-care and feels worthy of taking time for herself. To embody this new identity, this 2.0 version of yourself, you must fully let go of the old beliefs.

Below I will show you a technique we use in The Helix Method® to release deep-rooted beliefs energetically. We call this the Four Steps of Energy Kinesiology. These methods are used in various energy modalities and have become a regular part of my life and work. We use them to release beliefs, resistance, trauma and trapped emotions.

Focus on You:
Releasing Beliefs Using the Four Steps of Energy Kinesiology

If you would prefer to watch a short video taking you through these four steps, you can do so at https://foodfreedomfairy.com/the-4-steps-of-energy-kinesiology/

STEP 1 – You Ask a Question and Muscle Test

Muscle testing (or the sway test) allows you to unlock your subconscious mind and ask your body to help guide you with answers.

Stand with your feet hip-width apart, then close your eyes and relax your knees. Take a moment to go within and focus your attention on your heart.

Now set the intention that if you sway forward, it means yes, and if you sway backwards, it means no.

Now say out loud, "My name is (insert name)," and wait for your sway.

You will feel a forward pull, indicating, "Yes."

I encourage you to get used to trusting your sway first, so you can try with other statements. Choose ideas that you know the answer to. They should have yes or no answers. "I am twenty-one years old," or, "I drive a yellow car," or, "I have three cats."

Once you feel confident with your sway, you can muscle test the area you'd like to focus on.

Let's check in with a common belief around weight.

Example: "I will always struggle with my weight."

I imagine most reading this book will sway forward for a yes.

STEP 2 – Listen to Your Subconscious and Your Somatic Response

Check in with how you are feeling.

This step is about listening to your subconscious; it will speak to you through your body.

How do you feel? Describe what this belief feels like in your body. Where is it?

What can you see in your mind when you think about the belief?

Do you see a picture when you close your eyes? Describe what is happening in the picture. Doing this will help you connect with the belief to sense when you have let it go.

STEP 3 – Through the Power of Intention, You Release this Resistance

Now you're clear about what it feels like in your body or what the picture looks like, you can release this resistance through intention and breathwork.

The script framework is below.

You will say it three times, the first time out loud, followed by the second two internally.

Before you speak, take three deep breaths, breathing in for four and out for four.

Draw your attention again to the centre of your heart.

Say out loud:

"I am ready to release the belief I will always struggle with my weight that I can feel (insert where you feel any tension). I release this from all planes, times, dimensions and all levels of consciousness."

(This means releasing this across all aspects of reality and all levels of your consciousness.)

Take another deep breath in and out. Each time you breathe out, set the intention you are releasing the belief. Imagine it leaving your body and mind.

Say internally (twice):

"I am ready to release the belief I will always struggle with my weight that I can feel (insert where you feel any tension). I release this from all planes, times, dimensions and all levels of consciousness."

You can check that you have released your belief by confirming with a muscle test.

Once you are standing, ready to check in your sway, simply ask, "Have I released the belief I will always struggle with my weight?"

If yes, then you can move to step four.

If no, repeat this part of the process.

STEP 4 – You Align and Manifest

This is where you are changing your reality and where you imprint onto your human wi-fi the belief, thought, pattern and experience you intend to bring yourself into resonance with.

Just imagine the radio you have listened to for years no longer plays the songs that light you up. You are now tuning into a new station, a new frequency, that will make you want to dance at every opportunity.

When aligning your energy, you are imprinting your new belief or thought pattern onto your subconscious mind and human wi-fi.

To help you do this, you can create a short activation to use daily. This is a simple statement that you can read aloud each day.

For example:
"I am now at peace with my body and weight. I feel relaxed and happy. I allow this into my being across all planes, times, dimensions and all levels of consciousness."

Create your own using the outcome you desire and the feeling that you will feel once you have achieved this goal.

I am (insert outcome you would like).
This may be something like, I am now at peace with food, I am now eating to nourish my body, or I am now at my optimum weight.

I feel (insert emotions you will feel when you have this).
How will you feel? Overjoyed? Excited? Calm? Satisfied? Peaceful? Accomplished?

I allow this into my being across all planes, times, dimensions and all levels of consciousness.

Once you have created this activation, take some deep breaths and focus on the feeling of unconditional love. (Breathing in for four and out for four.)

Wait until you can feel this energy, and then say your statement out loud once and internally twice.

Summary of the Four Steps with Energy Kinesiology

STEP 1: You ask the question and muscle test with the sway technique.

STEP 2: Listen to your subconscious.

STEP 3: Release the resistance through intention.

STEP 4: Imprint onto your human wi-fi that which you want to create.

 **Focus on You:**
Aligning Weight Loss

Once you have released beliefs no longer serving you, I recommend creating a daily alignment practice. This will help you tune into that frequency of losing weight with ease and speed. The power of a consistent alignment process is not to be underestimated!

Successful manifesting includes seeing yourself achieving your goal before it happens.

Denis Waitley said in *The Secret* by Rhonda Byrne, "When you visualise, then you materialise. If you've been there in the mind, you'll go there in the body."

Using this technique, you will be gradually reprogramming the neural pathways in your brain. At present, your neural pathways hold information about how challenging your relationship with food is and how hard it is to lose weight. Not to mention the other programmes you may have running, such as food makes me feel better or keeps me safe. Neural pathways are responsible for various cognitive and behavioural functions, including decision-making. And, as we know, most decisions will occur from your subconscious mind. Hence, you must modify your automatic thinking patterns to be that of someone who has already found peace with food.

Using the activation statement you created in the last exercise ("I am now... I feel..."), I invite you to say this out loud for at least two minutes daily.

As you repeat the words, make sure you visualise the version of you that has already achieved her weight loss goals.

Choose a piece of instrumental music that will accompany your practice. This will help you lean into the feelings. Ensure you allow yourself to explore the feelings or, should I say, the frequency of this version of you.

Another tip from The Helix Method® is to 'live in the energy of the question'. Often, we send questions out into the universe, asking, "Why is it so hard to lose weight?" and we receive back all the reasons why it is damn hard! So, how about you live in the energy of, "Why is it so easy to be at peace with food?" Just send

At present, your neural pathways hold information about how challenging your relationship with food is.

that question out each day and see what answers come back. I like to write the question down daily and then see what ideas pop into my head. The ideas sometimes come throughout the day, so be patient.

And finally, it is important to remember that no matter how many times you visualise yourself as a smaller person, you still need to take action. You still need to choose to eat nourishing food, challenge your emotional pulls to food and so on. However, by aligning your energy each day, it will become easier. You will find that you are more 'in flow'. This energy will carry you forward to making choices that are more aligned with the upgraded version of you.

Daily Practice:

- Play your instrumental music.
- Take some deep breaths and focus on the version of you that is at peace with food.
- Say your activation statement out loud (repeating for at least two minutes).
- Live in the energy of "Why is it so easy to be at peace with food?"
- Take aligned action.

CHAPTER 10

Empowering You

You now have some of the tools necessary to embrace this change. You may already be using these strategies to raise your awareness around food, appreciate your amazingness and release some of your limiting beliefs. Or, maybe you have decided to digest the whole book first and then get to work. Either way, I want this book to contain words that empower you to take action. Reading the book is only the tip of the iceberg. True magic happens when you begin to implement what you learn. With this in mind, the following pages will discuss staying focused.

We will look at why you want to find peace with food. I know there are the obvious answers, but why does it really matter to you? Then you will create a goal and plan to help you stay focused and work towards the version of you that no longer worries about calories or weight. I appreciate the phrase 'goal setting' can be overused, and it can be tempting to skip ahead and think, "I know my goal!" And I get it! You want to get ahead to the sections you don't know, and goal setting can feel tedious. However, I promise you this is another vital step towards food freedom. With every goal, you need a clear, well-thought-out plan. Otherwise, your

True magic happens when you begin to implement what you learn.

goal is just a dream. And finally, we will touch on forming new habits, which is an essential part of the change process.

First, let's explore why you want to make these changes. What would finding peace with food give you? How would you feel if you no longer had the daily battle in your mind? If you woke each morning and your first thought wasn't a worry about food and weight?

Focus on You:
Finding Your Why

I invite you to reflect on the questions below. Please grab your notepad and pen to write down your answers. The questions may seem the same; however, the sentence prompts help you to uncover the layers and find your true 'why'.

Before you begin, I invite you to take several deep breaths to ground yourself. Allow yourself enough space to connect within and listen to your thoughts.

Breathe.

What is it that I really want to achieve?
Be clear and realistic.

Why do I want to achieve this?
Start your answer with: Because I think…

Why else do I want to achieve this?
Because I feel…

Why else do I want to achieve this?
Because I believe…

What happens if I don't make these changes?
How will my life look in five years' time if I don't make these changes? How will I feel?

Once you feel you have given enough thought to your answers, notice what feels most relevant. Are there any words or sentences that stand out or that you have written several times?

Next, I invite you to write a 'why' statement. Your why should be meaningful to you. It should inspire and motivate you.

Here is an example:

"I want to change my relationship with food and myself to feel confident and comfortable in my body. I want to increase my energy levels to run around with Nancy. I want to show my daughter how to have a healthy relationship with food."

Keep your 'why' statement to hand so you can read it back when you hear those thoughts creeping in telling you that your goal doesn't matter today!

A Goal and a Plan

Now I want you to get clear on your goal and how you are going to get there. Whether you are a seasoned goal-setter or you have never set a goal in your life, it doesn't matter. All you need to know is that statistics show that having a goal and a plan increases the likelihood of success in achieving what you want. In fact, various studies claim that people who write down their goals and create a plan are up to 50% more likely to achieve their goals than those who don't.

Saying, "I want to lose weight," or, "I want to think differently about food," is one thing – doing it is another. It is like saying I want to write a book and sitting down and writing down the opening page but never returning to it. Your desire is there, you want to do it, but you are not clear about how you will do it. How will the book be structured? When will you make time to write it? How will you publish it? Without a plan, it's just a wish.

How many times have you started a diet? Five times? Ten times? Forty times? And how many of those times did you have a clear goal and a firm plan? (Apart from, "I want to lose three stone by Christmas.") Often our goal can be a little wishy-washy. 'I am going to lose weight' is not really (and I am sorry, I know it is an overused phrase) a smart goal, nor does it give you a foolproof plan.

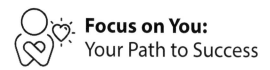 **Focus on You:**
Your Path to Success

Use the questions below to help you formulate your goal and a plan.

What is my goal?
(E.g., To lose weight, to find peace with food, to feel confident, to love myself unconditionally.)

By when do I want to achieve this?
(Set a date – your date can be moveable, and a goal such as a peaceful relationship with food is an ongoing process, but it is still helpful to have a date to measure and review.)

How will I know when I have achieved this?
(How can you measure your success? Is it a feeling? A size?)

How will I achieve this?
(What do you need to do daily or weekly? What new habits and practices do you need to include in your life?)

What times/days can I commit to doing what I need to do?
(Be clear, when will you meal prep, go for a walk, or spend time on yourself?)

What might get in my way?
(Predicting the obstacles means you can work around them!)

How can I ensure I get past these obstacles?
(Do you need to ask for help? What support might you need?)

I encourage you to be flexible and realistic with your timeline. I appreciate that when it comes to weight loss, we can often approach it with a deadline of a specific date, maybe a wedding or family holiday, but sometimes life gets in the way. Then when we don't achieve our goal, we can feel frustrated and a failure. I often ask my clients, "Is your goal weight loss or to have long-term peace with food?" Losing weight for a wedding or holiday is great, but what happens after the event? For most, the weight goes back on. I have seen it so many times. Rather than focusing on deadlines and weight loss, aim for changing your relationship with food and with yourself forever.

Habits

Our lives are made up of a series of unconscious habits; these habits become our automatic behaviour. What habits have you formed around food? Is it normal for you to grab a high-sugar snack after work because you are starving and can't wait until your meal is cooked? Maybe you always consume giant bags of crisps on a Friday night whilst watching a film or an oversized breakfast on weekends. Maybe the snack you have with your morning coffee has changed from fruit to biscuits. Or maybe your portions have gradually increased. Weight gain is rarely because we overate on holiday and didn't get it back off. Weight gain is gradual and made up of many small habits we have developed around our eating and our lifestyle. These unhealthy habits no longer serve you and small changes can lead to huge results.

Hardeep's Story

My client Hardeep had a habit of going to her favourite coffee shop to meet her friend Tracy twice a week for a latte and muffin. Hardeep told me she would love to be able to meet her bestie and make different food choices but she didn't feel she had the willpower. I asked Hardeep what she most enjoyed about going to the coffee shop. Her initial thought was that she looked forward to the delicious latte and sugary muffin. But as we explored this, Hardeep recognised whilst having the latte and muffin was enjoyable, she really enjoyed the time with her friend. She liked catching up, and talking to her friend always made her feel better if she was having a bad day. The thing is we all need this type of connection with others; it is incredible how thirty minutes with a friend can boost your mood and energy levels! There was no way Hardeep wanted to give up her twice weekly catch ups and she didn't need to! She recognised the human interaction was what she most enjoyed. Whilst the sugar hit was nice, it wasn't necessary. The calorie-laden latte and muffin had just become a habit, it was additional calories that her body didn't need, and the sugar wasn't serving her, so she chose to change her order.

Don't get me wrong, there were days when Hardeep thought blow it! And this is okay! Blow-it moments are an excellent opportunity to learn. I encouraged Hardeep to explore these moments with questions like, "What feeling or experience was I hoping to gain from eating the muffin?" And, "What problem did I think it would solve?" Or, "Did eating the muffin have the outcome I desired?" If it did, great!

If it didn't, that is okay too. May I also add that sometimes Hardeep ate the muffin for pure pleasure and that is okay. I will talk about pleasure foods later.

If you would like to add new habits into your daily routine then you may wish to try habit stacking. James Clear, writer of Atomic Habits[15] *suggests placing a new habit directly after an old habit so that it becomes second nature. For example, if you wanted to start taking daily vitamins, you may put them by your kettle. Your habit stack would be taking your vitamin pills after you switch on the kettle. By doing this, you will likely remember to take your vitamins – you have stacked a new habit on top of an existing one.*

We often think we have to go all in and radically change everything at once but that isn't necessary. You can alter your relationship with yourself and food by changing one habit at a time.

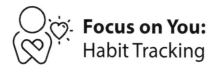

Focus on You:
Habit Tracking

What new habits could you add to your daily or weekly routine? Meal prepping, journaling, movement, working on the activities in this book or even checking in with someone for accountability. Make sure you make it as easy as possible. Leave your gym kit out the night before, prepare food for busy days, schedule time in your diary so there are fewer barriers. Hang the dog lead by the front door so you can grab it when you get home from work and go straight back out to avoid walking through the house and into the kitchen for a snack. All these small things will help you instil new habits. They are small, but they still take conscious effort, which is why we need a plan. Your default settings and ingrained habits may be lurking in the background for a while, so put in place whatever will help you.

I find habit trackers a helpful tool to monitor progress and accountability.

Below is an example of a simple habit tracker tick sheet. You can use an old-fashioned paper tracker, create a spreadsheet, or even use an app to track your progress.

	Mon	Tue	Wed	Thur	Fri	Sat	Sun
Daily walk	◯	◯	◯	◯	◯	◯	◯
Journaling	◯	◯	◯	◯	◯	◯	◯
Nourishment	◯	◯	◯	◯	◯	◯	◯
Self-care	◯	◯	◯	◯	◯	◯	◯
Water	◯	◯	◯	◯	◯	◯	◯

CHAPTER 11

Others and You

What you consume isn't just about the food you eat. Think about everything you ingest through your eyes and ears too. From the people you talk to, the books you read, social media you scroll through and programmes you watch. All of this has an impact on your views on food, body image and weight. In this chapter, we will focus on our relationships. From partners to family, friends and work colleagues. Why? Because as you may already be aware, some of them will likely influence your behaviour around food. (And your thoughts and feelings about all this stuff!)

Earlier, we explored your belief system and how to reframe unhelpful beliefs. But what about everyone else? Each person you spend time with has their own belief system, their own views about food. What's more, some will even have an opinion on what you should and shouldn't eat. Often these people will happily comment on your appearance and body size too. Commenting on another person's food intake or appearance is not acceptable; unfortunately, this is another part of diet culture that needs to be stamped out. Having said that, when I lost weight I *did* want others to comment,

What you consume isn't just about the food you eat. Think about everything you ingest through your eyes and ears too.

because at that time in my life I correlated my worth to my size. Sometimes others' opinions are helpful and valid; other times, it can make us question and even doubt what we know to be true. With this in mind, before you listen too closely to someone else's opinion, make sure they share the same values as you. Notice whether they are likely to encourage and respect your journey. Maybe they have already accomplished what you are striving to achieve and therefore can show you the way. Or do they make negative comments because they are invested in you staying where you are? Maybe you changing unsettles them. Or they could be stuck in the 'my life is not my responsibility' camp and want to keep you as their teammate.

At this stage, it is helpful to review your relationships with other people. Don't worry, I am not asking you to ditch your friends. You will see from the following examples this is about managing others and seeking support. From family and friends to partners and work colleagues, hopefully with your help they can enhance your food freedom journey.

Friends, Family and Colleagues

I remember when I started losing weight. My friends and particularly my work colleagues quickly fell into two camps. The 'Negative Nellies' and the 'Positive Pennys'! The Negative Nellies would say things like, "Are you still on that diet?" Or, "Don't you think you have lost enough now?" Or, "That isn't good for you. If you lose weight quickly, you will put it back on quickly!" Whereas the Positive Pennys would say, "Fair play to you, I admire you!" Or, "You do what works for you. We are all different." In the early days, depending on my frame of mind, the Negative Nellies could easily make me question what I was doing. And we all know this type of thinking can easily sway us!

Thankfully, I had the support of my coach, who helped me step back and look at the situation from the outside. I realised that those who were comfortable with who they were as a person were happy and accepting whatever I chose to do. Eric Berne, creator of the parent, adult and child ego states[16], would call this an 'adult' relationship. "I'm okay – you're okay." Neither of us is better nor worse; we each have our own opinions, which is okay. You do you, and I'll do me. Now the Negative Nellies were quick to share their thoughts, and looking from the outside, it was usually – if not always – because they were unhappy with themselves or their current situation and maybe not ready to change or didn't know how to. The Nellies were not necessarily dissatisfied with their weight (yes, some of them were, and some didn't want me to be the smaller friend), but many just had other things going on. They were unhappy in their work or relationships or stuck in a rut. You see, when another person steps up, it can make the Nellies feel like they should be doing the same. Their discomfort leads them to criticise, and most don't even realise they are doing it! In addition, we have those who make throwaway comments such as, "You are never going to eat all of that, are you?!" Or, "That looks like it could feed a family of four." These phrases make me squirm, my internal dialogue whispering, *That person thinks I am greedy and shouldn't eat this.* Later in this chapter, I will invite you to reflect on those people you spend most of your time with and whether you need to protect your energy from the Negative Nellies.

Parents

I often see fraught relationships with parents regarding food. Many feel they have the right to openly comment on weight, shape, size, food choices and everything in between. Over the years, many clients have spoken about the challenges of managing draining conversations in these areas.

Natalie's Story

Natalie was in her early fifties when she came to work with me. During our first session, she talked about her relationship with her mum. She told me she wanted to protect herself from her mum as she would sabotage her progress. When I asked Natalie what she meant by that, she shared how she would comment on her weight every time she visited, which left Natalie feeling like her size was more important than anything else. She said she always thought she was a disappointment, the fat daughter. This often led Natalie to eating crisps and chocolate on her way home. Her mother would also comment on what she ate. "Should you be eating that?" was the standard question. The irony was Natalie's mother would also encourage her to eat! If they went for a coffee, she would not have a cake unless Natalie had one. Even if Natalie didn't want to, she would eat it to keep the peace.

I asked Natalie if she had ever talked with her mother about this.

Was her mum aware of how hurtful her comments were? Did she know the mixed messages she was giving her daughter? Natalie knew she couldn't avoid her mother forever and needed a long-term solution. She decided to have a heart-to-heart with her mother, to be honest with her about her challenges with her weight. It was an emotional conversation as she told her mum that she had tried countless diets over the years. The fact that she had never changed jobs because she couldn't bear the thought of being judged at an interview because of her size.

And to her amazement, her mother said, "I didn't think your weight bothered you that much. You always seem so happy."

Natalie was in disbelief. How could her mother get it so wrong? She then asked, "When you comment on my weight, do you think it helps me?"

She looked confused. "Do I do that a lot?"

"Yes," Natalie replied, "every time I am here."

"Oh." Natalie's mother sat in thought. "I suppose I think it will remind you that you need to be aware of it. I worry about your health."

Natalie looked at her mum with tears streaming down her face. Natalie's mum realised the years of pain her daughter had gone through.

Natalie told me it was a relief to finally talk to her mother honestly and it was the catalyst that changed their relationship. They both agreed on some ground rules; her mother promised she would no longer pass comments on weight, size or food. Natalie knew this would be hard for her, and occasionally there was an automatic flippant comment, to which Natalie gave her a look of 'what did we agree?' and her mum quickly apologised, recognising what she had said.

Over the next twelve months, Natalie continued to discuss her thoughts and feelings about food with her mum. They explored how her beliefs were formed in her early years and smiled at those passed down from grandparents and previous generations. Natalie no longer avoids visiting her mother and has transformed her food habits.

Every relationship is unique, and I appreciate that we cannot all have deep, honest and sometimes frank conversations with our parents. However, this is one example of how speaking out can sometimes help others to reflect and understand their beliefs and behaviour. If you feel one of your parents triggers you or plays an unhelpful part in your relationship with food, then the important thing is to keep this in your awareness. As you continue with your self-development, notice others' comments are purely their opinion and a reflection of themselves, not you. You will need to find your own way to manage each situation. A powerful shift is letting go of the acceptance we can crave from our parents. This can take time; you may wish to seek support if you need to work through this.

Partners

Your partner, the person you have chosen to spend your life with, will again have their own unique relationship with food. They may have an 'eat to live' attitude and little emotional attachment to how food makes them feel. On the flip side, they may struggle just like you do, and together you are 'eating buddies', making lavish meals for each other because you both love food. Or saying 'I will if you will' when the dessert menu comes out! Then we have the annoying partners who seem to eat whatever they want and never gain an ounce, whilst you feel that you only have to sniff their plate to gain several pounds. Or maybe they do go up and down a few pounds, but they are disciplined in pulling themselves back to their happy weight. You may feel irritated if your partner does not understand what it is like to battle with food. (If so, please pass this book to them when you have finished!) You may choose to talk to them like Natalie and her mother. You may feel frustrated if your partner eats calorific food whilst you 'can't', and you may even find that your partner encourages you to eat because they prefer you as you are. Some also like to be the provider of food. It is their role within the home.

Some partners are also heavily invested in their other halves staying overweight. Partners who buy family-size bars of chocolate or bottles of wine the same week you announce your new diet. Partners who cook elaborate meals, buy cakes and book restaurants to reward weight loss.

Maria and Robert's Story

Maria was forty-three. She had been married to Robert for eight years. Maria had a busy life, and a thriving career. She also had a complicated relationship with food. She had lost weight countless times, but it always returned. The couple had a huge social circle mainly due to Maria's work. They would often be invited out for dinner parties or weekends away.

Robert hadn't come from a big family, he was an only child. He wasn't always comfortable in large social gatherings, but he would go to support Maria. He often sat quietly at the table, smiling and being polite but wondering when the night would end so he could return to his home. Robert preferred it when it was just him and Maria. This was his comfort zone. He loved to cook for Maria; he felt his role was to make sure that she had delicious food to enjoy after a long day. There would always be dessert too. Not one but a variety. And Robert knew Maria found it hard to choose, and she would often end up eating both. This pleased Robert as he felt useful, and this was the best way he could provide. It made him feel needed and it was his purpose within the relationship.

Robert had noticed that when Maria gained weight, she was uncomfortable going out; she struggled to find clothes she felt happy in. Because of this, they would leave early, and sometimes, Maria would suggest they didn't go.

As Robert often felt socially awkward, this worked well for him. It would have suited him never to go at all. He was happier at home, just the two of them, where it felt safe. On the other hand, when Maria did lose weight, or more to the point when Maria felt she was managing her relationship with food, she became more confident, she glowed from the inside, she gave off a beam of light saying, 'I am at one with who I am, I look and feel amazing!'

Whilst Robert was happy for Maria – he wanted her to be happy – this didn't sit well with him; somewhere deep down, Robert worried that Maria would become so happy that she wouldn't need him in her life and that she would have an affair or leave him for someone better looking and more confident. So, in an attempt to protect their relationship, Robert would step up his game in the kitchen. He would cook Maria's favourite foods even though she had asked him not to. He would fill the cupboards with Maria's favourite go-to snacks to sway her off course.

When I met Maria, she was already aware that this was

happening. She had even considered leaving Robert as she knew he was continuously sabotaging her efforts to lose weight. This may sound extreme, but Maria knew something had to change.

Maria and I explored the situation from Robert's point of view. We talked about how Robert might be thinking and feeling. I asked her if she had ever spoken to him about how he could support her with her weight loss. Maria said that any conversations around food were heated and often started with her being frustrated that Robert had cooked too much or bought high-sugar food for her. He would then defend himself and say, "You don't need to lose weight. I love you the way you are." Maria decided to sit down with Robert and have an open and honest conversation about how she felt about her health and why she needed his support to make changes. He admitted he felt safe when it was just the two of them and he feared that she may one day leave him. She reassured him that her love for him would not change with her weight loss. Robert agreed to support Maria.

This was a slow transition for both of them. Maria found pleasure in food; she had used it as a coping strategy for over twenty years. Robert had to lean into his new role and find new ways to express his love. Sometimes he would still offer Maria a cake with her cup of tea. Maria had to work on listening to her body's needs and saying 'no thank you' if she didn't want it. Maria and Robert are continuing to work together on leading a healthier lifestyle.

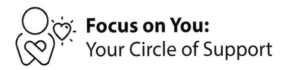 **Focus on You:**
Your Circle of Support

Now that we have considered the various relationships we have in our lives, I invite you to think about the people in your life. From partners to parents and siblings, friends and colleagues. Spend some time thinking about each person, what their relationship with food is like and whether they support you on your quest for food freedom. Remember each person is different and will have their own beliefs which shape how they talk about weight and food. It is not for us to judge or concern ourselves with this. In fact, you may find it helpful to work on detaching yourself from what others do. How others choose to eat is not our responsibility. Be curious, learn from them but don't judge or compare yourself. This activity is to help you create your support network. Bringing this into your awareness means that you are conscious and able to choose who you spend your time with and how you react to conversations around food, diets and weight. I often talk to my clients about bringing people into our world. Those close to us may find it hard to support us if they don't understand or relate to having a disordered relationship with food. You may wish to identify a person that you can 'bring into your world', someone you completely trust and feel you can be open and honest with.

Partner, family member, friend or colleague	Are they supportive of your quest for food freedom?	What is their relationship with food like? Can I learn from them?	Moving forward
Partner	*They do not comment.*	*Has no food issues.*	*Offer this book to read and ask for support – I need to think about what this support looks like and be clear.*
Mum	*Sometimes, but can often criticise and make comments about my weight.*	*She is pretty controlled about her choices. Has a healthy relationship with food.*	*Ask her not to comment or ignore her comments; I know that it is just her way of trying to encourage me to lose weight and be more health conscious.*
Jill (sister)	*Yes, we have similar issues with food but can also lead each other astray.*	*Similar to mine.*	*Discuss with Jill how we can really support each other and what other support we might need.*

| Rupi (work colleague and friend) | No, she constantly moans that I am dieting again and tells me it won't work and I am fine as I am. | She seems controlled, and brings a healthy lunch each day. I do wonder if she doesn't like the idea of me being smaller than her. | Politely ask Rupi if it is okay if we don't discuss weight loss anymore. I know she will be okay with this. |

Life is easier when we surround ourselves with people who lift us up. Jim Rohn is widely attributed as saying, "We are the average of the five people we spend the most time with." In other words, we become like the people we surround ourselves with. So, if your workday is spent with three Negative Nellies telling you there is no point in trying to lose weight, your best friend wants to eat fried foods each time you meet, and your partner drinks most days and encourages you to share a nightly bottle of wine, how would that work out for you? On the flip side, wouldn't things be easier if all your conversations about food were positive and focused on how easy it was to live a healthy lifestyle? Okay, I am not suggesting you ditch your friends, partners or colleagues (although you can if you feel you need to!). I simply invite you to be aware of your circle and, if needed, step back and smile at your awareness whilst you take what some say with a pinch of salt.

Life is easier when we surround ourselves with people who lift us up.

CHAPTER 12

Lifestyle Choices and You

In addition to the deep mindset work set out in this book, I wanted to share some simple lifestyle tools that we all know, yet are often are overlooked. The crazy thing is, these three actions have a significant impact on our overall health. Getting enough sleep, staying hydrated and keeping active are fundamental to your body thriving. However, it is surprising how many of us don't drink enough water, get enough sleep or do more than 4000 steps a day. As our lifestyles have evolved, we have fast-paced lives yet sedentary jobs, we work long hours, and downtime for many is scrolling social media. This means basic health needs are no longer being met. Your body will do its best to let you know it needs something, but unfortunately, that signal may be misinterpreted. For example, you may confuse thirst with hunger or crave sugar to keep going when you just need to sleep. Being out of tune with these needs has an impact on our body's overall health and ability to flourish. Over the following pages, we will touch on sleep, hydration and movement, why they are all equally important, and how we can ensure we get the right amount. And if the talk of moving your body more triggers

Getting enough sleep, staying hydrated and keeping active are fundamental to your body thriving.

you to want to throw this book out the window, don't despair; we will be reframing all things exercise.

Sleeping Habits

We have all experienced the effects of poor sleep, whether you have chosen to stay up late binge-watching the latest series or lost track of time scrolling social media (again), you have small children, your hormones are playing havoc, or you have not been able to drift off because something is on your mind. When you drag yourself out of bed in the morning, your concentration levels are poor, everything feels more of an effort; and your low mood means you become agitated by the smallest of things. Being sleep-deprived not only causes our stress hormone cortisol to rise, but it also increases the hunger hormone called ghrelin. Ghrelin compels you to seek out nourishment. It also acts on your brain's pleasure receptors, so you are more likely to reach for that something sweet to give you a boost, and your brain likes to play out this pleasure repeatedly. We will talk about being on this blood sugar roller coaster later. When our body is tired and running on empty, we lack focus and motivation, whether it is that walk you promised yourself or cooking a nutritious meal. It is easier to reach for something quick and processed when exhaustion kicks in and then zone out whilst unconsciously eating. We probably won't chew, taste or enjoy it either! Aside from this, your body needs adequate time to rest and repair. Research shows that when we get enough sleep regularly, we are less likely to be at risk of high blood pressure, diabetes, strokes and heart conditions. Health professionals recommend between seven and nine hours of sleep a night. You may find having less sleep works for you, however, seven-to-nine hours is generally optimum for your well-being.

So, what is your sleep like? Do you usually go to bed at a reasonable hour? Or do you set the intention to have an early night but then scroll on your phone for two hours? Lack of sleep has an impact on our hunger levels and mood. Addressing this could be a game changer if you regularly lack sleep. Some factors that may affect you drifting off to dreamland are eating late, drinking too much caffeine, working late into the evening, using your phone and watching TV – particularly the news or intense programmes that get your heart racing. And, of course, hormones can play a part in our sleep patterns too.

If you feel this is an area you need to address, then let's get you set up for successful sleep. You may have heard of some or even all of these tips before, but have you used them consistently for more than a day or two? Changing your habits requires doing it continuously until your subconscious mind does it without thinking.

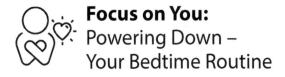

Focus on You:
Powering Down –
Your Bedtime Routine

If you struggle getting to sleep for whatever reason, I recommend creating some time to prepare your body for sleep. JJ Virgin promotes a 'power down hour'[17].

A time in which you signal to your body and mind to power down. We create rituals around children's bedtimes. Parents often create this routine within weeks of having their baby, so they understand it is time to relax their body and mind. Whether a child has a story, a little chat about their day, a bath, or they listen to calming sounds, it all helps power down after a stimulating day.

As adults, we can do the same. Your power down hour starts an hour before bed, but if you are busy in the evenings or an hour feels too long, make it thirty or even fifteen minutes; as long as you feel set for a successful night's sleep, it doesn't matter. Below are some things I have used and share with my clients to help them prepare to sleep.

1. Plan your sleep – how much do you need? Decide what time you need to go to bed to wake up and feel fully refreshed. This may take a few weeks to work out, but you will feel the benefit once you have found your routine.

2. Working backwards from your bedtime, set a time to switch off your TV and phone. If you aim to sleep by 11pm, you may choose to switch off the electronics at 10pm. Scrolling in bed is a definite no! I know it is difficult, but we all know that blue light sets our brain whirling! Please also consider the content you are consuming before bed. For example, if you are watching a film that has you on the edge of your seat and sets your

heart racing, does that affect how you switch off?

3. Take off your makeup, moisturise and massage your face. A simple self-care ritual will signal that it is time to switch off, and your skin will thank you!

4. Do some light stretches and deep breathing – even if this is just for a couple of minutes to signal that this is a relaxing time for your body.

5. Journal about your day and write your to-dos for tomorrow. Emptying your brain, reflecting on the day and planning for tomorrow means your mind has had time to process and is free to relax.

6. Meditate. It is another fantastic way to relax your whole system – mind, body and soul. Just five minutes is enough if you don't want to set aside any longer.

7. Make sure your sleeping area is as clutter-free as possible, so it feels like a relaxing space.

Staying Hydrated

If you are an avid water drinker, this section may not be relevant, but it is a good reminder of why keeping that water flowing is so important. As you probably know, staying hydrated is essential to maintaining good health. Water aids in regulating your body temperature, digestion, flushing out toxins, and transporting nutrients throughout the body. If you drink little water, your body may be working harder to perform these functions. Feeling sluggish, headaches and tiredness can all be linked to poor hydration. However, if you do not notice any issues, you may not see the need to increase your water intake. But what if I told you water is a big part of the metabolic process? (I am sure we all want our metabolism to work effectively!) If our metabolism works more efficiently, our body will burn more calories! Dehydration can slow down our metabolism and make it harder for our body to carry out its metabolic processes efficiently.

When dehydrated, there can also be confusion between thirst and hunger, leading to reaching for food over water and, therefore, the potential to eat more calories than needed.

Focus on You: Are You Drinking Enough?

The amount of water a person needs daily will vary depending on weight, age and activity levels. Guidelines can be confusing and misleading. In the UK, the NHS recommends six to eight glasses or around 1.2 litres daily, whereas the European Food Information Council recommends 1.6 litres for women and 2 litres for men.

As the term suggests, they are guidelines, and when you start getting to know your body, you will hopefully be able to tune into whether you need more water. Another way to check you're hydrated is by looking at your urine. If it is dark, you are likely not drinking enough.

If you feel you need to increase your water intake, here are some tips:

1. Drink a glass of water before each meal.
2. If you are a big tea or coffee drinker, switch some for hot water.
3. Opt for water over soft drinks.
4. Set a reminder on your phone to nudge you to drink.
5. Get into the habit of carrying a water bottle around.

Getting Moving (Please Hear Me Out First!)

If you have heard 'eat less and move more' for half your life, then it is no surprise if exercise has become a way to punish yourself after eating that slice of cake. Or a tool to burn calories, hoping the scales will drop an extra pound or two. If your quest for weight loss has left you with an unhealthy relationship with exercise, I hope we can change that. You are not alone if you have joined a gym only to go once or purchased an exercise bike that became a clothes horse. I have bought and sold three treadmills over the years, each time vowing to develop my love for running, and it just hasn't happened! Exercise wasn't part of my identity. I grew up in the eighties. My parents worked incredibly hard; my mum was of the generation where women began juggling mum duties and a career. Life was busy, and neither of my parents exercised regularly. My dad played football in his younger years, but he didn't replace that movement once he stepped down from the team. The only memories I have of my mum exercising was when we both went to keep fit classes, and this was to help me lose weight as a teenager. So, for me, exercise was not something my family did and, therefore, not something that I learnt is part of living a healthy life. When I say it is not part of my identity, it genuinely wasn't until recent years. I have had to find a way to enjoy moving my body, and if I am honest, I am still very much working on this now. Some days I still must push myself to show up for training, and some days, I still skip it.

 **Focus on You:**
Reframing Exercise

Okay, let's reframe exercise. (By the way, if you already love moving your body, feel free to skip the rest of this chapter!) We will start with letting go of the *word* exercise! Erase it from your vocabulary if needs be! I like to use the word movement with my clients. I would love you to think about movement as a tool that helps you live a healthy life. I don't know about you, but I want to get on the floor with my grandchildren and chase my great-grandchildren around the garden with the water gun when I am in my eighties! I find it far more helpful to think about movement in terms of keeping my body healthy. Keeping my body moving means I get to live an active life. I can walk my daughter to school without

Okay, let's reframe exercise. We will start with letting go of the *word* exercise! Erase it from your vocabulary if needs be!

feeling breathless, jump on her trampoline, go to theme parks and have the stamina to walk around all day. I don't have the desire to run 10km daily or climb a mountain. If that floats your boat, that is amazing; it's just not my bag.

I also encourage you to explore whether knowing how many calories you burn is helpful. I am talking to those who have watches that (probably inaccurately) tell you what your walk has equated to. All you need to know is that you move an adequate amount each day and have goals to increase your activity level where needed. I invite you to let go of your unhelpful beliefs, such as 'I should exercise', and allow in new thoughts around learning to find new ways to move your body that you love.

Think about the benefits of being active – aside from burning calories. Moving our bodies is incredibly important for our health and our well-being. Moving your body will increase your serotonin and dopamine levels. This releases stress and anxiety and improves our mood. I am sure you don't need me to tell you that staying active improves sleep. It also helps our lymphatic system to work, stokes our metabolism, improves our digestion, helps with muscle building, helps our immune system and helps the body get rid of toxins and waste. It really is about so much more than burning calories! I know 'you will feel better for it' is a cliché, but you honestly will.

To me, I have to make movement fun, too. What can you do that you enjoy? Does a stroll in the park feel pleasurable, or some stretches? Do you like dancing when you are doing the housework? Are you better when you do things with friends to keep you accountable? I love walking with friends for this reason. Now we even walk in the rain and laugh at how wet we get.

I would love for you to create your own 'movement menu'. This menu is your unique list of movement options. If you haven't moved your body in a while and are less mobile, start by choosing activities that last ten minutes or less and build up to longer bursts when you feel ready. Maybe think about what you enjoyed doing as a child. Roller-skating? Dancing? Trampolining? Swimming? Ensure your menu is full of things that make you smile, that you want to do. Because let's face it – if you hate the gym but you are forcing yourself to go four times a week, it isn't likely to last! I want you to reach a place where you look forward to that walk with friends, that stretch or aqua fitness class.

How do you ensure movement becomes a part of your life? Well, there is some effort on your part required when you are not feeling like it. But there are things you can do to ensure you get your movement in. Firstly, plan when you will move. Adding the sessions to your weekly diary means you are more likely to do them. Make them non-negotiable, just like your meetings at work or your child's football training. Tell yourself that booking something else and skipping the session is not an option. Again, it is easier to do this if you are doing something you want to do. I love my dance class, as we giggle at how uncoordinated we all are. For me, it is not an option to pop a client in that space or forgo the class to do something else.

Another helpful tool, as mentioned earlier, is James Clear's 'habit stacking'. Make sure your new movement follows things you do each day. Slip that walk in straight after you eat lunch. If you go swimming three days a week after work, put your swimwear in the car, and make your drive home a direct route to the pool rather than going home and coming back out. Don't give yourself the option to sit on the sofa and go back and forth in your mind as to whether you want to go.

Whilst writing this book, I have formed a new habit of waking at 5am. I journal and meditate whilst drinking a litre of water. At 6am, I make a cup of tea and I write from 6am to 7am. Then on the mornings my partner can wake our daughter and give her breakfast, I walk or swim 7–8am. I choose to do this because I struggle to find time in the day. I often only have school hours – 9am to 3pm – to work, so I find other pockets of my day to be productive. I didn't always find it easy to get up early, but it was something I wanted to do, so I was excited to get up and work on this book. On days when I do struggle, I use the *5 Second Rule* created by Mel Robbins[18]. This strategy is super helpful when it comes to doing things that you don't feel like doing. Mel Robbins explains that she first started to use the five-second rule to get out of bed at a difficult time for her. The process is simple. Count backwards from five, then immediately act at the end of the count, before the mind creates a reason not to. It creates a process to combat the subconscious mind and forces us to act on our ideas, whether it is getting out of bed in the morning, putting off a work call or getting out of the door to go for that walk. We all know how easy it is to talk ourselves out of things. Counting down from five, like a rocket launch, helps to get you going. Apparently, any longer than five seconds and the brain has a chance to stop you. Mel says counting down is key because, if you count upwards, you can continue to count!

To recap:
- Choose activities you like doing! (Don't commit to joining a gym if it's not for you.)
- Get a buddy! Do stuff with a friend so you keep each other accountable.
- If you need to, you can start small.
- Plan it into your day.
- Habit stack your movement onto other things you regularly do.
- Use Mel Robbins' *5 Second Rule*.
- Make sure you take note of how good you feel for doing it.

CHAPTER 13

Food and You

I wasn't sure whether to include any food guidance in my book. One, because I genuinely believe that most of my readers will already be very well-educated when it comes to food. Two, because it is rarely about food. And three, if you wanted to read a book about what to eat, you would have bought that book! With this in mind, over the following few pages, I will share some strategies you can use to explore your food choices. Choice is the optimum word here. Everything that passes your lips is your choice. I am sure I have said it before, but *you* need to be in the driving seat to change your relationship with food, not the diet! I do not give out meal plans or tell any of my clients what to eat. I prefer to invite them and you to develop a way of eating that you can adjust and tweak as you become the expert in your body's needs. I encourage you to think about eating for longevity rather than eating to fit into the dress or swimsuit for this year's holiday.

Some health experts advocate eliminating food groups, fasting or specific ways of eating, but when you are repairing your relationship with food, rules and restriction is not the answer. At a later stage, you may choose to let go of foods

Some health experts advocate eliminating food groups, fasting or specific ways of eating, but when you are repairing your relationship with food, rules and restriction is not the answer.

that no longer serve you. You may even dive deep into your nutritional needs. However, the emphasis needs to be on finding peace with food first.

Can You Let Go of Dieting?

What if the answer to all your problems was never to diet again?

How would you feel if I asked you to abandon all dieting rules for three months? How would you feel? A sense of dread? Do the alarm bells ring, saying, "No, if I don't diet, I will be twice the size!" Or have you already let dieting go?

Let's look at it another way. When you think of the word diet, what thoughts follow? How do you feel if you tell yourself, "On Monday, I am starting my diet again." Miserable? Frustrated? Suddenly hungry? Is there some excitement as you think, *This is it, I am going to do it this time, I will lose this weight,* followed by dread? The thing is, 'diet' is a negative word for those who struggle with food. It brings up thoughts of restriction, being unable to eat the foods you love and not being able to enjoy yourself.

In the Cambridge Dictionary, the first definition of the word 'diet' is: "the food and drink usually eaten or drunk by a person or group." You may, for example, follow a 'vegan diet' or a 'plant-based diet'. However, unfortunately, over the years, diet has become, and I quote, "an eating plan in which someone eats less food, or only particular types of food, because they want to become thinner or for medical reasons."

For many serial dieters, there is security in a diet. Some of my clients have felt genuine fear when I have even suggested they step back from dieting. Diets can feel like the only way we can control our weight; it's like a safety net that you can hop on and off whenever you think you are out of control. But it is the hopping on and off that doesn't work. Each time we step off the diet, there is a relief of not being restricted anymore. The green light signals to say you can eat anything. Enjoy! Even if we vow not to do this, our subconscious mind slowly slips back into its old patterns with food until we gain weight, feel miserable and eventually restart the diet. It's like we punish ourselves for overeating, for gaining weight. The punishment is to starve our bodies once more.

A Way of Eating for Life

How about working out a way of eating for the rest of your life? A food framework that you can develop as you learn more about yourself, your body's needs and your hunger levels. Could you get a little curious about what you are eating? Treat your body as a science experiment. Learn and evaluate your progress along the way. Could you get excited about that? I hope so because that is what will give you ultimate food freedom! Why? Because from now on, I invite you to make up the rules. And bend them to suit you! This means you don't have to wait until the weekend to step off your plan. If you want to have a cake on a Wednesday, you can! I know this may feel scary at first, letting go of the rule book, and that is why I have created a framework for you to follow to keep you safe.

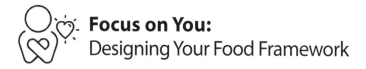

Focus on You:
Designing Your Food Framework

First, I invite you to make a list of all the food and drink you regularly consume, from daily meals to snacks, trips to cafes, nights out and takeaways.

List of food I regularly consume

Once you have created this list, you will divide it into three groups. Before you fill the chart in, please read the notes below.

The food you love eating that nourishes your body	The food you love eating but has little nutritional **value** – you are choosing to continue eating it because it brings you pleasure!	The food you are leaving behind because it doesn't have any nutritional value / doesn't bring you pleasure

Column 1: The food you love eating that nourishes your body

In the first column add all of the food from your list that nourishes your body. For example, any veg, fruits, meat, fish, dairy, nuts, seeds, pulses, etc., will go here. Include foods you are unsure of; you can tweak these later. This list will be your primary fuel source, so spend some time on it, and consider additional foods you would like to add.

Column 2: The food you love eating but has little nutritional value – you are choosing to continue eating it because it brings you pleasure!

In the second column, I want you to think about foods you love eating but maybe they do not serve your body as well. This may include highly processed foods and foods high in sugar, such as cakes, biscuits, crisps and crackers. It may be that giant bowl of pasta with a creamy sauce that tastes so good but leaves you feeling over-full and bloated. This list is the foods you choose to eat for pleasure, even though you know they don't serve your body as well as those in your first list. Notice I am not suggesting there is a food you do not eat; I am just asking you to be mindful of how they serve your body.

When you create this list, I want you to be picky. So, if you love a bag of crisps like me, be specific about them. What crisps are they? Is it a traditional potato-based crisp? Does it have to be salt and vinegar, or are you more of a cheese and onion girl? Or do you prefer cheese puffs or bacon fries? Don't just write 'crisps', be specific. Why? Because I encourage you to have a framework where you can still eat foods you enjoy. Crisps could include so many varieties, and I am willing to bet if you like crisps, you have some clear favourites. I want you to savour and appreciate the crisps you *choose* to enjoy.

You may not be so bothered about crisps but love a piece of cake. What type of cake would you choose? Do you love homemade lemon drizzle, or would a chocolate fudge cake be more your thing? You may think, I just love all cakes! But I bet there is one you would choose above all. And we have all experienced ordering a cake and being disappointed, that dry piece of cake that should have been thrown away, but the shop chose to get an extra day out of it. For example, I love carrot cake or lemon cake. When I think about chocolate cake it is often quite sickly and I never feel I actually enjoy it as much as I thought I would. Whereas a lemon muffin with lemon goo inside never lets me down – this is top of my list! Creating this list enables you to be specific about the foods you will choose to enjoy. Rather than eating any cake offered, you can be a little more picky, thoughtful and conscious about your pleasure foods.

You may be shouting at this book right now, saying, "I love all [insert your food of choice]!" I invite you to think about this being a 'belief'. Something that you have told yourself for so many years that you now believe it to be true. But is it true? Do you love every single type of cake there is? Do you love ginger cake? Do you love cake with fruit in it? You may be saying, "Well, I would eat it if there was nothing else!" And there is the key. Why? Why eat the cake you don't particularly love just because there is nothing else? When we start choosing the foods we love, the food we can enjoy and savour, rather than foods we tell ourselves we love because of a belief we hold, we are on to something!

Focus on eating to nourish your body and choose foods you enjoy. In other words, don't keep eating something if it doesn't taste good or you don't feel it is serving you in any way. Whether that is for pleasure or nourishment. If you are in a restaurant and the food isn't as tasty as you expected it to be, leave it. Don't eat it, to be polite or not to cause a fuss. I know most of us have done this before and then, at the last mouthful, said, "I didn't enjoy that!" The old me would have done this all the time! Now I wonder why I wasted all those calories on something I was not even enjoying! (I don't like to think of food as calories, but again from years of dieting, it's hard not to!)

Please ensure you include alcohol and other drinks. If you are partial to a glass of wine, what type of wine is it? Choose to only drink the one you enjoy rather than settling for others that are second best.

Column 3: The food you are leaving behind because it doesn't have any nutritional value and doesn't bring you pleasure

Now the third column is food that you are happy to leave behind. You may eat food that doesn't bring you pleasure and/or nourish your body. An example here may be breakfast cereal. Perhaps you have eaten it for years because you were told that it was 'healthy' or 'a good start to the day', and maybe you have never actually enjoyed it. You just eat it because you believe it to be good for you. Well, I don't want you to eat anything you don't enjoy. Or maybe you do enjoy it but recently found out it is full of sugar, and you are happy to trade it in for something else.

Your lists are likely to be ever evolving. As you move through this process, you will become more and more curious about food, how it tastes and how you feel after eating it. Feel free to go back and revisit your lists at regular intervals.

Next, you will create your meal plan for the week ahead or at least a couple of days ahead. I appreciate that, for many of us, meal planning can feel like dieting, it can feel like a chore. So, I invite you to think of this as an experiment. You will be playing around with your plan to suit you. If the plan goes out of the window, it is an excellent opportunity to explore why and what caused you to stop following your plan. How can you ensure that you stay with your plan if this happens again? Allow yourself to be flexible. If one night you are unexpectedly invited out or working late and your plan changes, be adaptable and focus on still making choices that serve your body.

Remember, this is not a diet; this is your framework. If you are still resisting planning, I urge you to challenge this. You are working on changing your relationship with food. It is valuable to plan what you are eating in the early days. You will eventually find a routine that works for you. If you prefer not to plan meals Monday to Sunday, list two or three breakfasts, three or four lunches and five-to-ten evening meals that you will choose from during the week, depending on what you fancy.

There may be days when you eat from your plan, you enjoy it and feel nourished, and there may be other days when you choose to go off plan, which is okay. This is YOUR plan; you are choosing the food. The resistance to doing this may come from feeling like you are dieting, so keep reminding yourself that this is not a diet. This is you experimenting with food. Over the following few pages, I will share some more tools you can use to develop your relationship with yourself and food. Remember to implement them in your own time. I certainly don't want you to feel overwhelmed with information. You could add one new tool each week as you work out what feels right for you.

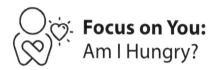 **Focus on You:**
Am I Hungry?

Do you currently honour your hunger? As a serial dieter, I often ignored my body's cues for food. I would skip meals, fill up on diet cola and eat small snacks for lunch to save calories. Skipping meals leads to intense hunger, and we are more likely to overeat. Your body sends out signals to say 'I am starving here! I need food'. And it is more likely to crave high-sugar foods as it is easier for the body to process straight into the bloodstream. Alternatively, you may be in the 'I can't remember when I was last hungry' camp and are therefore not receiving hunger cues.

I would love you to try using the hunger scale, but first, I invite you to think about where you feel hunger.

1. Where in your body do you feel hunger?
2. What does it feel like?
3. How do you know if it is physical hunger, an emotional need, or a habit?

Feel free to make some notes on this before moving on.

As you will see in the image on page 155, the scale is 1–10 (1 being not hungry at all and 10 being extremely hungry).

Aim to eat when you are at 7.

153

As a serial dieter,
I often ignored my
body's cues for food.

This means you should be preparing or thinking about getting food at 4 or 5. Ideally, you will be able to cook without wanting to pick because you are super hungry or purchase lunch without adding the extras because you are starving!

This scale is helpful for you to identify emotional hunger. What is going on if you notice you want food but are not physically hungry? Why do you want food? What do you think the food will do for you?

HUNGER SCALE

10	Starving, weak, dizzy
9	Uncomfortably hungry, agitated
8	Very hungry
7	**TIME TO EAT!**
6	Fairly hungry – could easily eat now
5	Moderate hunger
4	Mildly hungry – will want to eat soon
3	A little more hunger – think about preparing food or where to eat
2	Slight possible hunger
1	No hunger
0	Absolutely no hunger

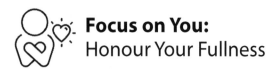

Focus on You:
Honour Your Fullness

As you learn to honour your hunger, honour your fullness too.

Take a moment to reflect on fullness. When do you eat until you are over-full?

Is it often in certain situations, such as in restaurants? Is it with certain types of food? Or when you are with certain people? Why do you think you do this? How do you feel?

FULLNESS SCALE

10	Completely stuffed – feeling sick!
9	Extremely full – bloated!
8	Over full – undo top button!
7	SATISFIED!
6	I have almost had enough
5	Moderately full
4	Mildly full but not quite finished
3	I know I have eaten a little
2	I have had a couple of bites
1	Yes still around the empty mark
0	I am empty!

In the same way of honouring your hunger, I would like you to honour your fullness.

On a scale of 1–10, 10 being completely stuffed, aim to eat until you are at 7.

You want to feel satisfied, not over-full.

If you go past 7, then it is an opportunity to learn.

During my learning, I noticed I was eating to 'find' fullness. I wanted to feel that fullness because it was what I had always known. There was something safe and comforting about that feeling. It is amazing what connections you find when you focus on your behaviour around food.

Remember to log your learnings to spot patterns and heighten your awareness. If you do eat until you're over-full, try not to criticise yourself. Remember, being cross and frustrated with yourself doesn't get you any further in your quest for food freedom. It only leaves you feeling worse. Instead, get curious and work out why. A habit? An emotional pull? Because the food tasted so good, you didn't want to leave it? Whatever the reason, reflect and move on.

Eat Consciously, with No Judgement, and Pay Attention!

As you settle into honouring your hunger and fullness, you will begin to understand your body on a deeper level. Again, see this experiment as an opportunity. Pay attention to your body's needs.

You are now learning to eat from a place of unconditional love. Your body and health are the most precious things you will ever have. Without good health, life is a lot harder! I also invite you to let go of any judgement about what you are eating. I appreciate I may have said this several times throughout this book, but I want you to remember it! If you choose to eat chocolate cake for lunch, no big deal, there is no judgement here. So what, it wasn't the balanced meal you had planned, but you didn't expect your friend to appear with a late birthday surprise. Just be curious. Explore your satisfaction levels; when you crave more, is it a physical need or an emotional longing? Does it sustain you until your next meal, or are you reaching for something else within an hour or two because your meal didn't fulfil you? Looking at your plate of food, would you say it is a balanced meal?

If you experience a mid-afternoon crash, is it your lunch choices that leave you craving a nap? Are there days when you feel alive and thriving? Is there a connection between how you feel and the food choices you have made?

It is also interesting to think about our attachments to food. It may be a simple memory, such as my nan and black forest gateaux, or my dad making piping hot soup when I was sick, or my great-gran peeling the mushrooms for our Sunday fry-up. When I eat any of these foods I am transported back in time and to those special people. Then there are crisps and diet cola. For me, it is like one doesn't go without the other. I have thought a lot about this combination and the fizz in my mouth, the salt with the drink. I also notice this is a habit,

As you settle into honouring your hunger and fullness, you will begin to understand your body on a deeper level.

a pick-me-up, an eleven o'clock thing. By the way, I would not encourage you to consume either of these daily, but it is another example of the rituals we create with food.

You are now ready to create a way of eating that does not include rules, counting calories or following a meal plan. You have tools to help you tune into your hunger, fullness and eat consciously. I hope thinking about food in this way has offered a different perspective on how to approach planning your meals. If you think there is room for improvement with your food choices or you feel physically hungry more often than you would like then the next chapter will support you with this.

CHAPTER 14

Tweaking Food and You

In the following pages, you will find simple strategies to help you review the framework you have created. As I said at the beginning of the book, I imagine many of my readers are well-educated on how to nourish their bodies. Therefore, the aim of this chapter is more of a reminder of the key points to consider for your overall health, well-being and weight loss. All health professionals will offer a similar message: limit processed food and eat more whole foods. As my relationship with food evolved, even though I knew this, I couldn't grasp it. Counting calories was so ingrained I would automatically add them up in my head. I did not think about the quality of my food choices or how satiating a plate of protein and vegetables was compared to a sandwich. It wasn't until I understood the 'blood sugar roller coaster' and reflected on the concept of eating like Farmer Giles that something clicked. Therefore, I hope sharing this information will resonate with you. I urge you to see this section as information to consume rather than rules to control what you consume! I know advice about what to eat can be a trigger for serial dieters, which

I urge you to see this section as information to consume rather than rules to control what you consume!

is certainly not my aim. Take what resonates and leave the rest!

1. Move towards Farmer Giles

Let me introduce you to eating like Farmer Giles. Carey Peters from The Health Coach Institute[19] presented this concept to me during my health coach training. It resonated with me as it was a simple approach to thinking and reviewing what you eat without counting calories, macros or using any other method.

In case you haven't guessed, Farmer Giles is a farmer! He lives on his farm with his family. They grow beautiful vegetables and fruit. They rear and nurture their animals. As a family, they cook and bake using their produce. They have a colourful diet. The cupboards are packed with various nuts, seeds, lentils, chickpeas, and whole grains, such as quinoa and brown rice. There is very little in the way of packets and tins in their kitchen cupboards.

Let's pop Farmer Giles on the left of this scale.

Farmer Giles   Little Miss Processed

Then we have Little Miss Processed. Her freezer and cupboards contain quick and easy processed foods to heat and eat. She shops unconsciously, buying what she has always bought. She is super conscious about calories but pays little attention to what is in the food. Little Miss Processed is exhausted from following diet rules, but she continues to battle on because she lives in hope that one day it will work for her, and she is petrified that if she stops counting, she will gain even more weight. So, wrapped up in calories, Little Miss Processed is less worried about the numerous ingredients added to her meal to make it last longer, taste and look better. The bright packaging and 'less fat/sugar' claims often draw her in. Little Miss Processed has never read anything more than the calorie count on the labels of the food she is buying. Let's pop Little Miss Processed over on the right side of the scale.

Okay, confession time: I spent years as a Little Miss Processed! I loved a chicken dipper or a fish finger sandwich (and still do)! My freezer used to be packed with food in breadcrumbs and oven chips. And a part of me still loves processed freezer food, but these days I would be more inclined to buy fresh fish and coat it myself rather than grab a box of eight in the supermarket. Now, my freezer is more likely to be full of frozen vegetables, especially chopped peppers, mushrooms and onions for days when I want a quick omelette. Plus, homemade soups, sauces and meals. There will always be days when I eat convenience foods, which is okay. Remember, unless you want to, you do not need to eradicate everything you previously ate.

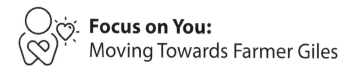

Focus on You:
Moving Towards Farmer Giles

Who are you more like? Where would you place yourself? Are you reasonably close to Farmer Giles and his family, or are you more like Little Miss Processed? Or maybe you sit midway between the two.

How often do you cook from fresh ingredients? There is no judgement here! It doesn't matter where you are right now. The question is, would you like to take steps to living more like Farmer Giles? Eating more like Farmer Giles will mean you are likely to eat foods that nourish your body and feel satisfied after your meals.

Questions for you to consider:

1. What can you do this week to eat more like Farmer Giles?
2. Could you aim to experiment once a week with a new recipe?
3. Could you batch cook so you have some go-to options?
4. Could you aim to be more mindful of the ingredients in the packaged food you buy?

It may be as simple as starting with one meal a week.

2. Carb Confusion and the Blood Sugar Roller Coaster!

Carbohydrates are essential to a healthy diet. However, they have gained a bad name over the past decade. With the popularity of low-carb diets growing online, slogans such as 'no carbs before Marbs' and celebrity endorsement, you may wonder whether you should avoid carbs altogether. Have you ever said, "I just can't eat carbs." I have to be honest, there was a period in my life when I felt the same. But it wasn't carbs that were the problem. It was processed foods (sugary carbs) that were causing upset in my body. There is a big difference between adding brown rice to my salad or a sweet potato to an evening meal than having several slices of bread twice a day and then a big bowl of white pasta.

Unfortunately, for many in the UK, the typical daily intake has become toast or cereal for breakfast, a sandwich for lunch and an evening meal loaded with potatoes, pasta or rice. This diet is not particularly high in protein or fibre; in other words, whilst you may have a little protein in your sandwich or with your pasta, it probably isn't enough. Furthermore, when eating these types and quantities of carbohydrates, there is little room left for goodness from vegetables, fruits, whole grains, nuts, seeds and legumes.

This isn't just about weight loss. This is about our health, including our mental health, not to mention the long-term damage this way of eating is doing to our bodies. When eating a diet high in carbohydrates and processed foods, your body is aboard the 'blood sugar roller coaster'. If you crave food every couple of hours and reach for sweet snacks to

This isn't just about weight loss.
This is about our health, including
our mental health, not to mention
the long-term damage this way of
eating is doing to our bodies.

get you through the afternoon, if you feel sick, shaky, dizzy, have brain fog and struggle to concentrate, then you may be on this ride. Because of the food industry and how our diet has evolved, this roller coaster has become very popular, certainly in the UK and US, with many riding, not even knowing they'd bought a ticket! Oh, and I forgot to mention it also affects your mood and emotions!

So, let's look at what is going on inside the body.

Please note: we are all unique in how we respond to food. Unless we delve into this more scientifically with tests and studies bespoke to each individual, our understanding of this can only be general guidance. However, for many who are eating a western diet, this advice could be life-changing.

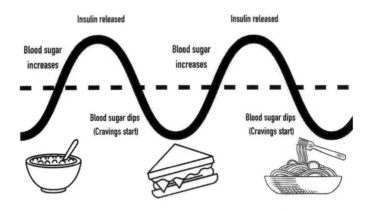

- When food is digested, the body's glucose level increases. (This is completely normal.)
- A glucose 'spike' refers to a significant increase in blood glucose levels after consuming a meal or drink high in

carbohydrates, particularly those that are quickly digested and absorbed.

- Foods quickly digested and absorbed tend to be higher on the glycaemic index (GI) scale. The scale ranks carbohydrates based on how quickly and significantly they raise blood glucose levels. (A list of foods in order of low-to-high GI can be found online.)
- When eating a balanced diet and mainly whole foods, this process tends to be more stable within our bodies. There is less of a spike because the food takes time to be digested and filtered into the bloodstream.
- When eating a highly processed diet (processed carbs, bread, pasta, biscuits, cake, etc.), then the sugar rushes into our bloodstream. The glucose spike is higher; additional insulin is produced to help manage the spike. As our body works hard to regain balance, we dip and experience the crash.
- That crash sensation can lead to us feeling discomfort, for example, dizziness, shakes and low mood. Or simply craving the same food every couple of hours. The body craves sugar as it is the quickest way to get glucose into the system again.
- And so, the cycle continues!

What is important to note is:
- Being in this cycle has a long-term impact on our physical health, not to mention our mental health.
- Being in this cycle also has an impact on our weight as we are more likely to overeat in response to sugar cravings and low moods.

- Higher insulin production can trigger our body to store more fat. (When our glycogen stores are full, insulin promotes the conversion of excess glucose into fat through lipogenesis. This stored fat can accumulate in adipose tissue, leading to weight gain over time.)

Now I love a good roller coaster ride; the anticipation during the climb to the top, my belly flipping as I descend at intense speed, and the twists and turns. If there is no queue, I would always go on more than once! However, after three or four times, I would feel sick. It is the same with the blood sugar roller coaster. Stay on it, and eventually, you will feel pretty naff!

When you continuously ride the blood sugar roller coaster, your body is constantly stressed. And aside from the long-term health impact, your body will always perform better when your blood sugar levels are steady.

So, how can you switch your ride to the slow train?

 **Focus on You:
Get off the Roller Coaster!**

If you need to get off the ride then, without overcomplicating things, follow these simple steps:

1. Eat protein with every meal.
2. Increase the number of vegetables you eat. Aim for vegetables to make up a third of your meal.
3. Eat healthy fats.

4. Be more selective with your carbohydrate choices. Aim to eat carbohydrates found in vegetables, legumes such as lentils and chickpeas, and grains such as quinoa, instead of bread, pasta, white rice, crackers and processed foods.
5. Try not to eat naked carbs! (Always pair with a little protein or healthy fats.)

Bonus tip: be aware that artificial sweeteners may also cause the same spike, so treat them like a sugar and pair with protein/healthy fats – or, alternatively, ditch them!

When supporting my clients with their diets, I am a big believer in adding in rather than taking away. As you increase your diet with more nourishing foods, you will feel more satisfied and have less desire for other foods. For many, counting and measuring feels like another diet, which is why I encourage you to focus on nourishing foods, listening to your body and recognising when you eat for reasons other than physical hunger.

Here are a few examples of how you may use this guidance:

*   Add eggs (protein) to your morning round of wholemeal toast.
*   Switch cereal (often high in sugar) to a protein-rich breakfast, such as a filled omelette (protein) or Greek yoghurt (protein) with nuts (healthy fat) and berries.
*   Create a Mediterranean breakfast board full of

tomatoes, cucumber (fibre), olives (healthy fat), hummus, meats and cheeses (protein).

- Eat fruit (high in natural sugar) after a meal to avoid the high glucose spike.
- If snacking on fruit, pair it with a handful of almonds (healthy fat).
- Add a side of protein to a lunchtime soup.
- Add hummus (protein) to your salad and sprinkle with some seeds or nuts (protein and healthy fat).
- Switch white pasta for wholegrain or try an alternative such as spiralised courgette (to increase fibre).
- Add lentils (protein) to soups.
- Switch sandwiches to an open sandwich piled with protein.
- Cook from fresh, whole ingredients whenever possible.
- Cook double and freeze portions for busy days.

Making small changes – like swapping high-sugar cereal for a protein-packed breakfast or a sandwich for a colourful high protein salad – will leave you satiated, and less likely to snack.

3. Read the Labels

If your focus has been counting calories, points or syns, you may have overlooked reading the ingredients on a label. However, if you are eating any packet food, I recommend you get curious about what it contains. Often, we are misled by claims such as 'high in fibre' or 'low in sugar'. It is easy to grab these products thinking you are making a 'good' choice. However, these are often marketing ploys. A packet of biscuits saying 35% less sugar will probably mean 35% less than their standard packet (which is incredibly high in sugar). A 'high protein' yoghurt may have slightly more protein than a regular yoghurt, but if you aim to increase protein, check exactly how much protein and compare it to others. Also, look at what else is in the yoghurt! A 'high protein' label doesn't mean it is not laden with sugar!

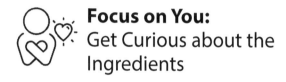

Focus on You: Get Curious about the Ingredients

If you are not label-savvy already, I invite you to spend the coming weeks exploring the contents of the products you regularly purchase.

1. Look at the ingredients rather than the claims on the front of the packaging.
2. Scan for recognisable whole foods. Be curious when faced with long ingredient lists, especially when they are words you haven't heard of (I love to google them!).
3. Note that the first ingredient makes up the majority of the product, followed in order of quantity. For example, a box of cereal's first

ingredient may be 'whole grains' and the second 'sugar', so sugar is the second highest ingredient in that box of cereal.

4. Check for hidden sugars, which can often be disguised under various names like high-fructose corn syrup or dextrose.

5. Be aware of serving size guidance.

CHAPTER 15

The Future You

I appreciate that you may still find yourself stuck even when armed with information, strategies and tools. You may be desperate to move forward, but you can't seem to find the motivation. You have a tonne of excuses, and they all seem valid. Or you find your flow for a while, but when something throws you off course, it's game over.

This recovery phase is like trying to find your way through a maze. You enter the maze full of excitement; it seems like a fun idea and looks relatively simple. You have been briefed on the layout and what to expect. However, as you try to find your way through, you come across dead ends and feel frustrated. Eventually, you feel lost. You consider returning to the start. But deep down, you know starting again is not an option. If you leave the maze through the entrance, you know you will be disappointed. Then you remember every dead end is an opportunity to learn. You know where not to go; you just have to remember! You decide to note them down. You leave clues to ensure that you don't repeat the same path. Eventually, you find your way. As you reach the exit, you feel amazing.

I would love you to find your way through the maze, so over the following pages, I will share some thoughts about motivation, willpower, the excuses we make, falling out of routine and getting out of your comfort zone. And of course, some strategies to help you.

Motivation and Willpower

You are now thinking about your relationship with food on a deeper level, but you are still wondering, "How do I stay motivated?" And I get it. You have spent years looking for the willpower and motivation to take you to your goal! The thing is we shouldn't need to 'find motivation'. We are all motivated to do things, it just depends if they are high on our values. I discovered this several years ago when I was introduced to Jason Graystone[20].

Jason is a trader, investor and entrepreneur. I love what Jason stands for – living life to your highest values. Finding your purpose, following your passion, sharing it with the world and not settling for anything less than an incredibly fulfilled life. Jason talked about willpower and motivation in a way I hadn't heard before.

He explains that we are motivated to do what we *want* to do. And do those things that are aligned with our highest values. If we don't hold our health or working on our eating habits high on our list of values, we are less likely to want to work on them. Therefore we would need to 'find the motivation' to change.

Let's look at some examples. Lola is motivated to go to

We are all motivated to do things, it just depends if they are high on our values.

the gym at 6am every morning. This is because she holds her health as one of her highest values. Her well-being is essential. She knows if she doesn't exercise, she will not feel as good mentally and physically, and this will affect the rest of her day. Occasionally, Lola considers turning over and going back to sleep, but she rarely does because she values her health. Lola doesn't need a tonne of motivation to get to the gym each day.

Kelly's children are the highest of her values. She is an awesome working mummy and will do anything to ensure her children are happy and cared for. Kelly puts her children's needs first, even if she has little time for herself. Kelly does not need motivation to take her children to the park or play with them. And after a long day of work and looking after her children, Kelly's downtime is watching the TV. She doesn't need motivation to chill out in front of the TV, but she definitely needs motivation to do her workout.

Judy, on the other hand, doesn't value watching TV. She sees it as dull and a waste of time when she could be working on her business. Judy adores her hair salon and has big plans for the future. Her business is one of her highest values; if she had some downtime, it would be reading or crafting. However, Judy will happily work late into the evening. Judy does not need any motivation to work as she loves building her business.

Can you see how we are motivated to do what we hold to our highest value? If your health isn't as high on your values as other areas of your life, you are less likely to feel motivated to eat nourishing foods or move your body. However, sometimes we forget that we can't do any of the things we love doing without our health and unfortunately many people only face this realisation when it is too late.

When I decided to write this book, I set a writing routine, and each day at 6am I wrote for an hour. I would wake at 5am to start my morning routine of meditation, journaling and gratitude. Did I need to be motivated to get up? No, I enjoyed getting up because I wanted to pour my heart into something I felt so passionate about. I would have laughed at you if you had asked me four years ago to get up at 5am each day! Yet now, I love climbing into bed early as I am genuinely excited to go to sleep so I can wake up and work on something meaningful. My highest value is to help women like me, to share what I have learnt. I am motivated because I am striving to reach as many women as possible who have been stuck in the dieting cycle.

To recap, we are motivated to do things we want to do and things that are aligned with our highest values. You don't need to find motivation. You need to align your goal to your values. Whilst there may be an element of discipline needed, when these are aligned, your journey to food freedom will be an easier one.

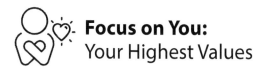

Focus on You:
Your Highest Values

If having a healthy relationship with food doesn't feel high on your values, attach your goal to something that is. Maybe you value being a parent, aunty or a grandparent more than anything else in your life.

Maybe you want to watch them grow and thrive, and you want them to have the most wonderful, pain-free life. (That's what we all want for our loved ones, right?) Well, having food freedom and a healthy relationship with yourself means that you are more likely to live a happier and potentially longer life. It also means you are showing others how to look after, nourish and be at peace with their body. You are ensuring they have healthy habits for their future.

Think about your highest values:
- What is it you value most in your life?
- What is most important? Family? Friends? Career? Freedom? Self-growth? Adventure? Creativity? Inner peace?
- How can you attach your weight loss and food freedom goals to these values?

For example:
- If you value being creative, how can you get creative with food, recipes or ways to move your body?
- If you value being spontaneous and adventurous, then can you find excitement in getting active outdoors, being spontaneous in the kitchen or visiting new restaurants?
- If you value your career, can your team work together to create a healthier workplace?
- If you value relationships, can you meal plan or cook together? Can you organise walks and picnics rather than TV and takeaways?

Excuses

Time for some tough love. There will always be excuses that stop you from reaching your goals; lack of time, willpower, money, or it is simply too hard? I encourage you to question them. Do you really not have the time, or could you manage your time better? If you often spend an hour a day on your phone, is that an hour you could spend working towards your food freedom goals? Do you honestly not have the money to eat healthier food? Could you look at your budget? Is there anywhere you are spending money unnecessarily? Whilst sometimes these excuses are real and genuine, there is always a choice on how we spend our time, money and energy.

I once asked a group to list the excuses they had used to overindulge in the past. We filled pages and pages on the flip chart! Many of the excuses came from limiting beliefs. As you become skilled at listening to your inner self, you can laugh at it and say, "Ah, here you are again, telling me I can't do this. Thank you for reminding me of my old thinking patterns. However, I am ready to move forward."

'I'll start when my diary is clear' is a common excuse. But unless we go into another lockdown, you will always have a busy diary. You need to learn to listen to your body in all situations, including social occasions and when busy. Remember, no food is off-limits. There is no restaurant in the world you can't go to. Plus, if it were the case that not having any social events and being confined to your home was the key to sorting out your relationship with food, then you would have cracked it during the lockdowns.

There will always be excuses that stop you from reaching your goals. I encourage you to question them.

Focus on You:
Ditch the Excuses

1. Spot the excuses – catch yourself! Learn to spot *when* you are making them. Remind your inner self that you hear her, offer her reassurance, and then continue with your plan.

2. Keep taking action. The best way to push past your excuses is to take action – just start! Do something each day to work towards a healthier relationship with food. This week, you may journal daily about your feelings after meals. This will help you make more informed choices. This is an easy task; you are not telling yourself you can't eat anything. Next week, you may decide to focus on getting off the blood sugar roller coaster. Again, no restrictions, no diets. You will never regret taking action, but you may regret allowing your excuses to ruin your progress.

Falling Out of the Routine

Unless you are incredibly disciplined, you will occasionally fall out of routine. If you prepare for this, you can learn to catch yourself and refocus.

Holidays are notorious for taking us out of sync. There was a time when I dreaded holidays as I didn't want to 'fall off the wagon'. But here is the thing: we don't necessarily gain a lot

You will never regret taking action, but you may regret allowing your excuses to ruin your progress.

of weight on holiday. It is what we do afterwards that has an impact on the scales. Yes, we may weigh heavier after a flight and eating more carbohydrates, higher-sugar foods and, for some, drinking alcohol. But this is water weight and glycogen and within a week of being home, that tends to rectify itself. At least it does if we return to eating to nourish our body. The thing is, we are prone to hopping on the scales and being so annoyed with what they say that it affects our mindset and what we then eat for the rest of the week… the month…or longer!

When I go on holiday, I eat differently. I eat at different times, and my activity levels change. If I am honest, I probably don't listen to my body as much as I would like to, I get carried away with the joy of being on holiday. I eat a lot of my pleasure foods that have less nutrition. And you know what, that is okay! I don't beat myself up. I don't come home and weigh myself anymore, either. What good would it do me? My memory of a fantastic holiday tarnished by the gain of 7lbs. I know it will disappear as I settle back into a routine. Is knowing the number of pounds I have gained going to help me? Personally, no, but for some, it may. As I said earlier in the book, if you use the scales, please remain logical and unattached to them.

I like to come home and focus on getting back into my normal routine. It is often harder the first week as my body is saying, *Hey, where is that delicious dessert that you gave me last week?* I want that sugar! But I know my body doesn't want it; it loves nutritious, wholesome food. It's just a little confused because it has been in holiday mode. I simply remind my body how we take care of ourselves.

If you are finding it difficult to reset, think about what worked for you when you were in flow, when everything was easy with food. Can you draw on some of those strategies? Maybe you have stopped journaling, and putting pen to paper again may enable you to refocus. Maybe meal prepping. Or asking for help. I will talk about support a little more over the coming pages.

The Downsides to Weight Loss

With any change, there may be a downside. It can be easy to think of all the benefits and good reasons for finding peace with food, but what about the disadvantages? What are the downsides to this journey? There will be some, even if you can't think of any immediately; with every change there are pros and cons. Sometimes the change feels so different we find ourselves in unknown territory. Our subconscious mind screaming: *We are going too fast, this is not safe!*

Ruth's Story

Meet Ruth, thirty-eight; she lived at home with her parents when we met, and she suffered from social anxiety. She did not leave the house; her days were spent with her mum and dad. Joining my group was a monumental step for Ruth. She felt the group work would help her move forward, not only with food but with her anxiety. Within the safety of the closed group, she explored her relationship with herself and with food. At first, Ruth would only speak to me one-to-one. Within the group, she would smile and listen but never voice her thoughts. After ten weeks, Ruth spoke aloud to the whole group for

Our subconscious mind screaming: We are going too fast, this is not safe!

the first time. I knew this was a huge milestone for her on the way to her new life. However, as Ruth lost weight, her family expected her to be able to go shopping and do 'normal' things. Her family assumed that she had lost her anxiety along with her weight. Ruth was not quite ready for this. Whilst she felt a million times better, this was just the start of her transformation; it was a gradual process that she was building on week by week. The pressure from her family felt overwhelming to Ruth, and somewhere, subconsciously, it was easier to return to a larger body. The layers were her protection; they kept her safe. Safe from having to be in situations where she didn't feel comfortable. The thing is, Ruth didn't spot this at first. She believed she had lost control of food; her inner self told her it was inevitable. Internally, she heard, "I told you that you wouldn't be able to keep it off. I don't know why you bothered!"

I see many women who have regained weight because they, subconsciously, feel safer. It is familiar. They may not have social anxiety, it may be they feel less visible in a larger body, they attract less attention, or they have promised themselves that once they tackle their relationship with food they will tackle other areas of their life.

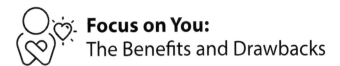

Focus on You:
The Benefits and Drawbacks

When making any change, there are always benefits and drawbacks. To maintain changes, the benefits need to outweigh the drawbacks.

- Spend a few minutes listing all the benefits of finding food freedom.

- Then list what you think the downsides or drawbacks are.

Often, there are thoughts lurking in our subconscious that can hold us back. Exploring this and recognising where you may be feeling discomfort is helpful. Bringing these thoughts into your awareness means you can start working through them.

Benefits of changing my relationship with food and myself	Drawbacks (or downsides) of changing my relationship with food and myself
• I will feel better in myself. • My health will improve. • I will not be out of breath when walking. • I will feel more confident at work and in social situations. • I will enjoy clothes shopping. • I will feel more confident in swimwear (and underwear). • I will be able to cross my legs. • Choosing daily outfits won't be stressful. • I will be able to walk miles on holiday. • I can take up horseriding again.	• I am worried I won't be able to eat what I want. • I am worried my relationships with others may change. • My friend may be jealous of my weight loss. • People will expect different things of me. • I may have loose skin.

It is also worth checking in with your list of drawbacks; sometimes they are just unhelpful thoughts, stories you are telling yourself, and with a little logical thinking, you can work through them.

To summarise, when you fall out of your routine, accept it as part of the process and make a conscious effort to get back into it as quickly as possible. Don't wait for motivation and willpower! Work out your highest values and what motivates you, then link your weight loss goals to that. Remember, there will always be an excuse; your subconscious mind is trying to keep you where you are, as it feels safer. Recognise and move forward, constantly checking in with and reassuring your inner self. You have a choice each day to manage your thoughts. You can choose which thoughts you listen to and select new thinking patterns. Become skilled at managing your thoughts, and you will become skilled at managing your relationship with food.

Become skilled at managing your thoughts, and you will become skilled at managing your relationship with food.

CHAPTER 16

Supporting You

Now that you have the tools and information, I encourage you to think about what support you need. If, like many of my clients, this battle with food has been weighing you down for many years, then, as you have seen, it requires a little more care and attention than most diets offer. We place pressure on ourselves to solve our disordered eating alone. However, it is a complex, multi-layered problem that often requires additional support, guidance and accountability.

How often have you told yourself, *I should be able to do this*. Then you have beaten yourself up because you fell off your diet. If you still think, *I should be able to do this myself*, then I would ask, "Why? Why 'should' you be able to do this yourself? Because you are successful in other areas of your life? Because you are fifty-three? Because you are a mother? Grandmother?" There is no real reason you can tell me I would believe! So please, stop trying to be strong and build a support network. You have already explored those close to you and their relationships towards food. Now it is time to look at who else can support you and how.

Accountability

For most, accountability is vital. That is why thousands attend weigh-ins in school halls every week. They know being weighed will keep them on track. (Although I appreciate that this is not always the case! The old me would have skipped a week to try and claw back some pounds, and then if I had not managed to do that, I would not go the following week!) However, that accountability is still there and works to a degree. Please note I am not suggesting you go to a meeting to weigh weekly; this is merely an example of accountability!

Having a personal cheerleader and accountability partner can be very motivating. Knowing you have a clear timeline until you see your coach or friend gives you a focus for your week. You know you are aiming to achieve what you have set out to do within the agreed time frame. With an accountability partner, you can agree on clear action steps for your week ahead and create a plan on how that will work. You have someone to problem-solve with too. Accountability creates consistency, and we know consistent actions produce results.

Types of Support

Let's think about what type of support you need and don't need.

As I mentioned previously, the people around us can have a significant impact on our eating. With this in mind, if you seek help from those closest to you, please consider

Accountability creates consistency, and we know consistent actions produce results.

how that help may look. A partner who doesn't want you to change may not be helpful. Neither will your work colleague who has tried every diet under the sun but is still struggling herself. Try to find someone who has been where you are and has walked the path. Someone who you aspire to be like, someone who you feel has the answers. Or at least someone who is willing to read this book and work through the process with you. This person must be non-judgemental and obviously want to support you.

The person or people you choose should be your biggest cheerleaders but also hold you accountable, remind you of your weekly or monthly goals and challenge you if you haven't completed them. Not in a critical way but from a place of curiosity, from a place of, "I wonder what is going on for you that you haven't completed the action steps you said you wanted to take this week?" This can be a big ask for people you are close to. The last thing you want is to damage a friendship because your friend challenges you, and you, in frustration, tell her to, "Get stuffed!"

Working with a Professional

I wanted to share a few thoughts for those considering working with a professional. The role of a coach is to support, listen, hold you accountable, challenge your thinking, empower you and celebrate your successes. If you choose to work with a coach, you need to feel confident they can hold the space for you as you transition through this change and into your new identity. Coaches will often offer a consultation before you agree to work with them. This is an essential part of the process for you and the coach. I would only choose to work with someone if they were ready to commit and I had the relevant skills to help them. A good coach with integrity will never try to convince you to work with them.

A coach's role isn't to dictate actions; it is to help you discover your own solutions. A skilled coach refrains from offering immediate advice and encourages you to make independent decisions. When the answer comes from within, you will feel empowered to take action. This often yields greater results than acting on advice that may feel forced and less productive.

Investing in you is one of the most powerful things you can do for yourself. This signals to your mind and body that you value yourself enough to seek support and help. By enlisting professional help, you also commit to taking the task seriously. Most, if not all, successful people have coaches. Whether a top athlete, an award-winning actor or a successful entrepreneur, they have sports coaches, acting coaches, or business coaches. Often, they have a team of people supporting them to be their best version. Whilst you may not be able to afford a team, if you recognise that you need the help and choose to work with a professional, your future self will thank you!

Conclusion

Now that you have read this book, I hope you have been reassured that where you are with your current relationship with food is not your fault, a diet will not solve your problems, you are not 'naughty' or 'bad' if you didn't stick to 1200 calories a day and you are not alone if you have wrapped yourself in cling film before your best friend's wedding! (If you know, you know!) I hope you have a clear path to take you on the road to food freedom. As you can see, it is possible to leave behind the dieting cycle, repair your relationship with food and yourself and live a life you love in a body you are grateful for. You now have a broader understanding of the tangled web weaved between food and many humans. You know that it is entirely normal to have developed a disordered relationship with food, and whilst it is unlikely that it is your fault this happened, it is your responsibility to change it.

I know it would be very easy, if you haven't entirely made a bestie out of your inner self, to allow her to pipe back up as you put this book down and say, "That was an interesting book, but I will never be able to change," or, "I wish I could be strong enough to work on this, but I am not." Please don't let this happen! You can do this!

You are not alone if you have wrapped yourself in cling film before your best friend's wedding!
(If you know, you know!)

If you haven't completed the activities throughout the book, I recommend you return to the beginning and do so. Taking action propels you forward. It cures fear and creates confidence and courage. On the other hand, inaction breeds doubt and fear.

You have the tools to work on your awareness, to uncover how you think about food and what you prefer eating rather than what has become a habit. You now know how to communicate with your inner self with compassion and love rather than arguing with her until you give in and eat the chocolate. We have looked at the importance of self-love and how, by increasing your self-worth, you will want to take better care of yourself. Self-love and care is about far more than candles and bubble baths; it is having clear boundaries with others and carving out time for you to do something that brings you joy.

You have also explored energy sources. Not only energy from our food but from sleep, movement and people. When you balance all of these, you will have an abundance of energy. When you create the support your mind and body needs, there will be no stopping you! You have released or know how to release limiting beliefs and install new ways of thinking that are more helpful. And you know how to tune in your human wi-fi so you can get in flow with all of the above!

It's Over to You!

As I draw this book to a close, I feel excited that I have finished it! However, I am even more excited for you. You may feel empowered because you have been implementing everything you have been reading, and you can already see the benefits. Or you may need to reread it to embed the information thoroughly. I recommend you write down your next steps and ensure you have accountability and support. I don't want you to find this book a year from now in your bedside drawer and remember the time you thought about making these changes. I want this book to become worn, and the edges of the pages curled over from its use. I have every faith that you can and will embrace food freedom. Why? Because I know deep down, like me, it is all you ever wanted.

I wish you every success on your journey; remember, I am still on mine. I am, like you, ever evolving and ever learning. It is not always easy, but it is definitely worth it.

With love,

jenny x

The Food Freedom Fairy

P.S. If you would like to hear more from me, sign up to receive my empowering food freedom emails at:

https://foodfreedomfairy.com/emails/

I have every faith that you can and will embrace food freedom.
Why?
Because I know deep down, like me, it is all you ever wanted.

Acknowledgements

To James for always believing in me, for being my 'rock'. For encouraging me to follow my dreams and to never give up. For reminding me, in my darkest of moments, 'this too shall pass'. You are my best friend and I will love you forever.

My daughter Nancy for being the most kind-hearted amazing little girl. Thank you for coming up with the name 'The Food Freedom Fairy®' and for being my biggest fan. You have constantly told me how incredible you think my book will be, which spurred me on, even when my subconscious mind was throwing unhelpful thoughts at me! I hope I always teach you that you are always more than good enough and that anything is possible.

To my mum and dad who have always strived to be the best parents a girl could wish for. And for asking me, 'When is your book out?' every week for the past twelve months. I love you both dearly.

To my bestie Kelly who has a heart of gold and is the voice of reason when I get myself into a pickle. I know you are always there for me, no matter what challenges you're facing on your own path.

To all my family and friends, too many to mention but to name a few, Cherie, Dan, Tracy and Mark, you guys always make sure I have something to look forward to. Thank you for always keeping my calendar full of exciting adventures. And to Emma and Michelle for our woodland walks (with and without the girls), for always supporting me and showing an interest in my work. A special shout-out to Emma for fact-checking my section on nutrition too.

Thank you to my amazing beta readers, I am grateful for your time and feedback which enabled me not only to improve my book but also gave me confidence that my words would be well received by those who need to hear them.

Thank you to Lucy McCarraher for being an awesome writing monitor, for holding me accountable and for creating the space for an inspiring group of women to become authors. Thank you to Jen at Fuzzy Flamingo for correcting my mistakes, making my manuscript look like a book and for your support and handholding through the entire publishing process. I could not have done this alone!

And finally to all my amazing clients who have allowed me to share their experiences. I hope you understand how valuable and relatable they are to my readers. You are an inspiration and I am forever grateful to have been a small part of your healing journey.

About the Author

Jenny McDonald, also known as 'The Food Freedom Fairy®' is on a mission to help women break free from the endless cycle of dieting and reconnect with both food and themselves.

Like many, Jenny struggled with a poor body image from an early age. She absorbed unhelpful messages about food and weight, which led to secret eating, shame and guilt.

In 2004, Jenny started to repair her relationship with food and lost over 40kg.

Finding a renewed sense of self, this transformation inspired Jenny to leave her career in theatre and enter the dieting industry.

Over time, Jenny noticed her clients were trapped in a cycle of dieting and she found herself using diet products to maintain her weight. This realisation prompted her to establish her coaching practice.

In 2020, Jenny released the *Power Over Food Podcast* and founded The Becoming You Academy®. Through the academy, she guides women in nurturing their mental, physical and emotional well-being. Her approach allows for guilt-free enjoyment of food. Most importantly, Jenny encourages clients to embrace self-love and appreciation.

Jenny is a certified and accredited health and life coach trained in CBT (cognitive behaviour therapy) and energy healing modalities, The Helix Method® and Theta Healing®. Her approach offers a holistic transformation for those seeking a genuine and lasting change.

To connect with Jenny and access her free resources, please visit www.foodfreedomfairy.com

Resources

Remember healing your relationship with food is a personal journey. If you feel you need additional support here are some organisations you may find helpful.

Beat
www.beateatingdisorders.org.uk/

Talk ED
www.talk-ed.org.uk/

Mind
www.mind.org.uk/

Samaritans
www.samaritans.org/

If you would like to continue your journey with me then please take a look at my group and individual coaching programmes.
www.foodfreedomfairy.com/work-with-me/

If you are looking for a therapist, the following websites are useful places to begin.

British Association for Counselling and Psychotherapy
www.bacp.co.uk/

The UK Council for Psychotherapy
www.psychotherapy.org.uk/

Lipoedema

If you think you may have lipoedema and would like more information and support please check out the following organisations and individuals who are all striving hard to raise awareness within the lipoedema community. This is by no means an exhaustive list.

UK

Lipoedema UK www.lipoedema.co.uk/
Talk Lipoedema www.talklipoedema.org/

SPAIN

ADPLA Aragòn www.adplaragon.org/

US

Fat Disorders Research Society www.fatdisorders.org/
Lipedema Simplified www.lipedema-simplified.org/

Lipedema Project www.lipedemaproject.org/
Lipedema Foundation www.lipedema.org/

AUSTRALIA

Lipoedema Australia www.lipoedema.org.au/

Podcasts

Lipoedema Mama Podcast
Living Well with Lipedema Podcast
The Lipoedema Podcast
Spotlight Lipdedema
Lipedema Link
The Lympha Press Podcast

Instagram Accounts

@the_lipedema_mama @lipoedema_lifestyle @kaztalks @
curvygirlbeth @virginiashealthcorner @lipedema_mamas_
podcast @the_lippy_lady @lipedemafitness @me_and_
my_lipoedema @the_lipoedema_podcast @drkarenherbst

References/ Further Reading

1 Földi, Michael and others, *Földi's Textbook of Lymphology for Physicians and Lymphedema Therapists* (München, Germany: Elsevier, Urban & Fischer Verlag, 2006)

2 Talk Lipoedema, 'About Lipoedema', 2023 <https://www.talklipoedema.org/about-lipoedema/> [accessed 14 January 2023]

3 Carl Baker, 'Obesity Statistics', Commonslibrary.parliament.uk, 1.3336 (2022) <https://commonslibrary.parliament.uk/research-briefings/sn03336/>

4 Richard V. Burkhauser and John Cawley, 'Beyond BMI: The Value of More Accurate Measures of Fatness and Obesity in Social Science Research', Journal of Health Economics, 27.2 (2008), 519–29 <10.1016/j.jhealeco.2007.05.005>

5 Kevin D. Hall and Scott Kahan, 'Maintenance of Lost Weight and Long-Term Management of Obesity', Medical Clinics of North America, 102.1 (2018), 183–97 <10.1016/j.mcna.2017.08.012>

6 Andrew Jenkinson, *Why We Eat (Too Much): The New Science of Appetite* (London: Penguin Life, 2020)

7 Julia Buckroyd, *Understanding Your Eating: How to Eat and Not Worry about It* (Berkshire: Mcgraw-Hill, 2011)

8 Dr. Eric Berne, *Transactional Analysis in Psychotherapy: A Systematic Individual and Social Psychiatry* (Souvenir Press, 1961)

9 Kristen Helmstetter, *Coffee Self-Talk* (Rodale Books, 2020)

10 Holly Matthews, *The Happy Me Project: The No-Nonsense Guide to Self-Development* (London: Green Tree, 2022)

11 Rhonda Byrne, *The Secret: The 10th Anniversary Edition* (New York: Atria Books 2016)

12 Roxie Nafousi, *Manifest* (Chronicle Prism, 2022)

13 Louisa Havers, 'The Helix Method', Louisahavers.com, 2023 <https://louisahavers.com/helix-method/>

14 Louisa Havers, 2023 <https://louisahavers.com/about-louisa/>

15 James Clear, *Atomic Habits: An Easy & Proven Way to Build Good Habits & Break Bad Ones* (New York: Penguin Audio, 2019)

16 Dr. Eric Berne, *Transactional Analysis in Psychotherapy;a Systematic Individual and Social Psychiatry* (Souvenir Press, 1961)

17 JJ Virgin, '7 Easy Ways to Fall & Stay Asleep', 2015 <https://jjvirgin. com/7-strategies-fall-stay-asleep/#:~:text=Create%20a%20 power%2Ddown%20hour> [accessed 9 August 2023]

18 Mel Robbins, *The 5 Second Rule: Transform Your Life, Work, and Confidence with Everyday Courage* (USA: Savio Republic, 2017)

19 Holistic Health and Wellness Training | Health Coach Institute <https://www.healthcoachinstitute.com> [accessed 9 August 2023]

20 Jason Graystone <https://www.jasongraystone.com/> [accessed 11 August 2023]

Printed in Great Britain
by Amazon

35946024R00123